SUBCORTICAL
MECHANISMS
OF
BEHAVIOR

BASIC TOPICS IN PSYCHOLOGY

Edwin G. Boring, EDITOR

PHYSIOLOGICAL PSYCHOLOGY

ROBERT A. MCCLEARY AND ROBERT Y. MOORE
Subcortical Mechanisms of Behavior

SUBCORTICAL MECHANISMS OF BEHAVIOR

THE PSYCHOLOGICAL FUNCTIONS OF PRIMITIVE PARTS OF THE BRAIN

Robert A. McCleary, *1923–*

AND

Robert Y. Moore

Basic Books, Inc.

PUBLISHERS

NEW YORK : LONDON

EDITOR'S FOREWORD

THE ENORMOUS GROWTH of scientific research and activity since World War II has included psychology as one of the recognized life sciences. Psychology now makes no small contribution to the rapid change in Western culture and civilization, a contribution that consists of a stream of new discoveries. There is also to be remembered, however, psychology's contribution to its own maintenance. That lies in teaching, for every academic generation must train the next. The roots of psychology must grow if the branches are to spread and the seeds of new growth germinate in the classroom. Research would ultimately exhaust itself were adequate prior training of the scientists deficient. That fact is now well recognized in principle, if not always in practice.

These short books are designed, in the first place, to make instruction easier. The ablest instructor is inevitably an individualist. He is never content to design his course to fit the idiosyncrasies of the other able man who wrote his textbook. A single text, moreover, seldom contains enough material to constitute all the reading a student needs. The instructor will wish to supplement his text and lectures and to have freedom in choosing what he shall add. The availability of many small books packed with solid reading enables the instructor to choose what he wants and makes their purchase by the student practicable.

The other use of these books is to satisfy the intellectual curiosity of intelligent laymen. They are not so technical that professional men and thinking women who are keeping an eye on the advance of civilization cannot use them to understand what the psychologists think and know. The philosopher, the historian, the lawyer, the physician, and the modern mother of grown children can surely employ these books in keeping up with the scientific times.

Physiological psychology is rapidly growing. Even the investigators are put to it to keep up with its advance. The subject as it was known ten years ago is already so outdated as to seem naïve. In these small texts, we have the current picture as it emerges from a mass of research to the view of these authors. Science keeps on becoming, said a famous Frenchman; these books show where small sections of it are now.

Edwin G. Boring

PREFACE

ALL PARTS of the brain excluding that evolutionary new-comer, the neocortex, can qualify as subcortical structures. There are thus hundreds of brain centers and nerve pathways, from the more primitive types of cortex in the cerebral hemi-spheres down to the bottom tip of the spinal cord, all of which could receive consideration in the pages that follow. The weight of the book in your hands indicates clearly that we have been highly selective. We have restricted our attention to four subcortical areas or systems: the hypothalamus, the ascending reticular formation, the reward and punishment zones, and the limbic system. Our justification for this choice is simply that these subcortical structures are four that have particularly stimulated the interest and research of the scien-tists dedicated to studying the problem of how the brain mediates behavior.

The intended readers of this book are advanced under-graduate and beginning graduate students—as well as the "intelligent layman," as he is called, who wishes for one reason or another to get some summary understanding of how the brain functions. With this intermediate audience in mind, bibliographic references have been kept to a minimum. Those scholars who know the sizable research literature that stands behind each of these brief summary chapters will recognize promptly the unacknowledged contributions of hundreds of investigators in many scientific disciplines. It is to these laboratory workers that authors of scientific books always owe their primary debt of gratitude.

We have tried to acquaint the reader with the names of the earlier investigators who, as things have turned out, can now be said to have pointed the way. Beyond this, with a few exceptions, our choice of references has been dictated by the pedagogic aim of supplying the interested student with additional survey material that will provide him a broad coverage in return for extra effort. These secondary reviews, for the most part, have extensive bibliographies from which the student can learn the value of digging back into the original experimental literature.

We wish to express our gratitude to Mrs. Violette Carasso for her assistance in the preparation of the bibliographies and in the typing of much of the manuscript and to Mrs. Renagene Preston who also willingly typed for us at several points along the way.

Robert A. McCleary
Robert Y. Moore

University of Chicago
January 1965

CONTENTS

SUBCORTICAL MECHANISMS OF BEHAVIOR

I

CORTEX
AND SUBCORTEX

UNTIL RECENTLY, the study of how the brain handles complex
behavior was almost exclusively focused on its uppermost covering layer—the *neocortex*. Scientists thought that the more
important kinds of mental function (thinking, remembering,
learning, and the like) were in some manner, at least for higher
animals and man, localized in the network of nerve cells that
make up the cortex, as the neocortex is more commonly
called. It is true that earlier there were some suggestions as to
the importance for behavior of the more primitive subcortical
portions of the forebrain (such as Herrick, 1933); yet faith
in the cortex as the prime controller of complex behavior persisted over the first half of the present century. This point of
view is still the common oversimplification of facts that greets
the reader of many beginning texts in psychology or such related disciplines as physiology and neurology.

Probably nothing was more influential in contributing to

this corticocentric point of view than the manner in which the brain developed in the course of evolution. The phylogenetic development of the brain thrust the expanding cortex forward and upward, both literally and figuratively. For one thing, this pattern of evolutionary development resulted in the cortex's being in a superficial position on top of the prominent cerebral hemispheres, a position within fairly easy reach of earlier investigators' surgical tools.

More important than this convenient availability of the cortex, however, was its enormous increase in size in the more advanced vertebrates. The lowly fish has no neocortex at all; the more advanced amphibians, reptiles, and birds show increasing amounts of cortex, and in mammals this part of the nervous system achieves its greatest relative size. This evolutionary pattern of development is called *corticalization,* and it reaches its peak in man. The conclusion to be drawn seemed clear to the earlier workers: since the higher animal forms with their apparent greater mental capacity were endowed with greater amounts of cortex, this enlarged top of the brain, so it appeared, must be principally responsible for more complex kinds of adaptive behavior.

On the other hand, it was necessary also to face the fact that the very simple invertebrates, as well as lower vertebrates with little or no cortex at all, can, for example, learn and remember new patterns of behavior. The fish, without any cortex, is even capable of stimulus generalization (i.e., fish can discriminate relations among stimuli, react to which stimulus is bigger or brighter), behavior that is regarded as a type of advanced perceptual ability in higher animal forms. Moreover, when measured on comparable tests of learning ability, fish and other simpler vertebrates require an amount of training that compares favorably with the well-cortexed subhuman mammals.

Nevertheless, both the anatomical and behavioral facts seemed to be adequately explained by the notion that, along with the obvious increase in the amount of cortex in higher animals, there was also an upward shift of functional control within the brain. Since corticalization obviously took place anatomically, it seemed reasonable to suppose that behavioral capacities originally handled by parts of the brain beneath the cortex in simpler animals were in some undefined manner "taken over" by the expanded neocortex of more advanced vertebrates. The idea was that a broad *functional* corticalization had gone along phylogenetically with the obvious *anatomical* corticalization. There is, indeed, some experimental support for this point of view.

For example, if one restricts his attention to the motor areas of the cortex, the facts fit these traditional expectations fairly well. In more complex animals, damage to cortical motor areas is clearly more disastrous to motor function than in lower animal forms. Rats—and even cats and dogs—show minimal and transitory loss of muscle function following total removal of cortical motor areas, while in monkeys the resulting motor loss is much more severe. Finally, the severe paralysis that can result in man from "stroke" damage, which involves motor cortex, is well known. Even in man, however, some degree of motor recovery can occur, and it is not yet certain whether it is a residue of cortical tissue or the subcortical centers that supply this returned function. That subcortical structures may have more motor capabilities than once was supposed is suggested by recent work with human patients in whom it was surgically necessary to cut the main outgoing pathway from the motor cortex (the *pyramidal tract*) on one side of the brain. After the shock effect of the surgical procedure had subsided, these patients still had a remarkable amount of motor ability in the limbs that were now largely isolated from direct motor control by the cortex. The patients walked satisfactorily and could even hop up and down on the affected leg.

The areas of the neocortex that receive various types of

sensory information, the so-called *primary sensory areas,* have also seemed more crucial in the behavior of the higher animals than in lower forms. Damage to these cortical areas results in increasingly severe sensory loss the more advanced the animal species. For example, the fish, without cortex, is capable of discriminating visually among objects that differ in brightness, color, or shape. In such mammals as the rat and cat, however, removing the primary visual area of the cortex results in distinct, though only partial, loss in visual ability. The greatest loss in such operated animals is evident when they are tested on complex perceptual problems that require them to discriminate between stimuli that differ in shape or pattern. Such cortically damaged animals also lose the simpler ability to perform a previously learned habit that was dependent on seeing a difference in brightness, but they can readily learn the habit again, even without their visual cortex. In fact, if the animals are required to use only a very simple flexion of the leg to indicate their recognition of the brightness difference, removal of visual cortex has no effect at all on the animals' performance, even if the habit was learned before surgery. In this case, the subcortical centers seem to be handling the entire behavioral sequence.

These findings have commonly been interpreted as meaning that, in the simpler mammals, the ability to respond appropriately to differences in brightness is in a transitional state so far as the cortex is concerned. It is as though the cortex had as yet become only partly involved with this simpler sensory capacity, so that the animal can still manage with only the appropriate subcortical center intact. Quite recently this subcortical center has been apparently identified (posterior thalamic nucleus), and, at least in the rat, workers have shown that the cortical and subcortical components are both normally involved when the animal is learning to discriminate among test objects of different brightnesses (Thompson,

1963). Even in the case of primary sensory ability, therefore, where the evidence for corticalization of function once seemed to be on the safest ground, there is growing reason to think that subcortical sensory centers may be making more substantial contributions than once was thought to be the case, at least in such animal forms as have been studied. It now appears that the cortical monopoly is not as great as was originally believed. For example, aside from the subcortical contribution to the ability to discriminate among different brightnesses, workers now report also that damage to the superior *colliculi* (another important subcortical visual center) can also influence the more complex ability of the rat to discriminate among different visual patterns.

In man, however, with his vastly expanded cortex, corticalization of visual function has seemed essentially final and complete. Without his visual cortex, man has no useful vision left at all. Except for another matter (discussed at the end of this chapter), you would be tempted to conclude that human vision is handled exclusively by the cortex.

There is also new reason to think that subcortical portions of the auditory system can process more complicated information than was previously supposed. For example, it is now known that a cat without its auditory cortex, while doing poorly at certain types of very complicated auditory task, can still manage subtle discriminations of pitch. Most surprising of all, these cortically damaged cats react spontaneously and appropriately to tones that differ exactly by an *octave* unit from the tone to which they were originally trained.

It is difficult to be certain of the exact effect of the total removal of auditory cortex in man. Such clinical cases as are available suggest that this type of brain damage in man results in total deafness. This statement, however, does not mean necessarily that, even in man, auditory function is handled exclusively by the auditory cortex.

It is even more dangerous to pin all one's faith on the cortex when considering behavior that is not primarily concerned with simple motor or basic sensory functions. Pure cortical lesions outside motor or sensory areas produce deficits in animals that are subtle rather than gross and dramatically evident. From Karl Lashley's pioneering series of behavioral studies of the functions of the rat's cortex in the 1920s to the many recent studies of the monkey's cortex, the story has always been the same: In the absence of sensory and motor loss, behavioral deficits in animals following various cortical lesions (even in the so-called *association areas*) are partial, sensitive to the amount of cortex removed, and generalized in nature. Sometimes the behavioral losses are only temporary. Cortical damage affects animal behavior adversely—of that there is no doubt; but the resulting deficiences in adaptive behavior are certainly not total losses of easily defined, complex abilities.

Except for human speech, which is highly sensitive to cortical damage, the story is similar at the level of man. There is probably no more instructive example than the cases of psychiatric patients subjected to psychosurgery of the cortex of the frontal lobe. This is a particularly interesting instance since, along with the idea that the cortex has taken over the control of higher mental processes, it is common to assume a further evolutionary process—*frontalization*. The thought here is that the frontal lobes, since they are so remarkably expanded in monkeys and man, must have emerged to control the most complicated behavioral processes of all. It is, for example, very common to find a published diagram of a brain in which the frontal lobes are clearly labeled "thinking." When one has accepted this idea uncritically, it is quite disappointing to find how little behavioral deficit in human patients results from surgical damage to their frontal cortices (*frontal lobectomy*) or from the severing of some of the connections between the frontal lobes and the rest of the brain (*frontal lobotomy*). While it is true that behavioral changes in such patients are discernible to trained observers, the changes consist in subtle deviations in the personality; they are not calamitous, over-all losses in any so basic a mental capacity as "thinking" or the ability to learn new material or solve problems.

From animal studies, in which more objective behavioral analysis is possible, damage to the frontal lobe has been said to interfere with the performance of tasks involving time delay or the proper execution of a temporal sequence of responses. Such operated animals tend also to be hyperactive and distractable, traits which could account for the other findings. At any rate, in neither man nor lower animals are there experimental findings to support the notion that frontal cortex, in any exclusive way, is involved with complex mental ability.

It seems best not to regard any one level of the brain as having sole control of particular behavioral functions, functions not shared or influenced to some extent by certain structures at other levels. Cortical and subcortical centers should be viewed as forming a highly interconnected system in which constituent parts share in contributing to the final form of a given behavioral performance. Moreover, as we shall see, it is usually more a matter of convenience than truth to consider separate parts of the brain in isolation. The brain is so redundantly interlocked that it is difficult to know where a given subsystem begins or ends.

Over-all Plan of
Cortical–Subcortical Connections

The question of the general nature of cortical–subcortical connections requires consideration before we focus on isolated subcortical centers. Behavioral scientists have had particular interest in one aspect of this question: whether neural pathways that connect cortical sensory areas with cortical motor areas are organized horizontally or vertically. While seeming to have little to do with the subcortex, this matter is of interest because it has to do with the type of functional relationship that exists between the cerebral cortex and the various lower brain centers that are our chief concern.

The idea that there is a *horizontal organization* is the older and more traditional point of view. The simplest form of this suggestion was that sensory information from the outside world arrived at the appropriate sensory area in the cortex, and nerve impulses then passed across the cortex (in so-called *transcortical paths*) to the motor portion of the cortex. Neural activity in this motor area was then presumed to produce an appropriate response over the well-known *pyramidal tracts* that eventually connect the motor cortex with the peripheral muscles. This view concerned itself principally with the neural activity between the stimulus and the motor response that occurred at the cortical level. Workers assumed that activity in the intervening *association areas* of the cortex would be sufficiently "enlightened" to assure an adaptive response. At the present time, however, a far more limited role for transcortical connections is suggested by the available experimental studies. The earlier confidence in horizontal organization matched the earlier emphasis on the cortex well. Although no one believed that the subcortical systems contributed nothing at all to the organization of behavior, it was nevertheless the transcortical connections that primarily interested these early workers as they tried to understand learned, complex behavior. Such isolated interest in the cortex also mirrored the general feeling that lower brain centers played only a supportive role, mediating primitive instinctual responses and simple reflex adjustments.

It was along with our newer understanding of the importance of subcortical systems in behavior that a different notion emerged about the possible functional relation between the cortex and the lower brain centers. This newer point of view emphasizes the *vertical organization* of the brain, an organization that involves up-and-down pathways—*loops,* as they are called—between lower centers and the cortex. Many such loops could be involved in any particular behavioral sequence as the subcortical and cortical activities bring into play appropriate circuits, some farther up and others farther down in the long axis of the central nervous system.

Such a form of vertical organization not only seems reasonable on general grounds, but recent experimental findings have also supported this idea in a more direct way. For example, Robert W. Doty (1961) and his co-workers attached electrodes to the skulls of cats in such a way that the electrical contacts rested superficially within the cortical layer or on the surface of the cortex. In the animals to be considered here, at least one such electrode was in the visual cortex and a second in the motor cortex. The motor electrode was located so that when it was used to apply electrical stimulation to the cortex, a discrete peripheral movement of one of the limbs occurred, one that easily could be observed by the investigators. Such *cortically induced movements* were used as the unconditioned response (UR), and electrical stimulation through the electrode in the visual area was used as the conditioned stimulus (CS). In the more usual conditioning experiment, the UR is a response that occurs automatically when a particular stimulus is used (e.g., when an animal's foot is shocked, the UR is a flexion of that leg). The CS would then be some stimulus other than the shock, e.g., a buzzer, that comes to produce the leg flexion only because it is presented a number of times along with the shock to the foot. Doty hoped, as in the usual conditioning experiment, that by repeatedly stimulating the visual electrode and the motor electrode one after the other, it would eventually be possible to produce the movement of the extremity when the visual electrode was activated alone. Conditioning (learning) of this type turned out to be possible but, while that fact is remarkable enough, it is the second stage of this experiment that for present purposes deserves the closest attention.

After successfully conditioning their cats, these workers surgically sectioned the cortex near the sensory electrode and retested for the conditioned response in order to find out over what neural route the new sensory–motor connections had been built. They used two types of surgical cut. Either they completely *circumscribed* the sensory electrode with a circular cut that went through the cortex or they *undercut* the spot of visual cortex in which the CS electrode was located. The main results can be described simply. When the electrode in the visual cortex was circumscribed and thus its direct transcortical connections with the motor cortex were severed, the conditioned response could still be obtained when the CS electrode was activated; when the cortex beneath this CS electrode was undercut surgically, and so lost its downward connections, stimulation with the CS electrode no longer resulted in the performance of the learned or conditioned response. While there are other experiments that demonstrate much the same point, this work is a striking example of the kind of animal research that has lent support to the idea of vertical organization within the central nervous system.

It is of course difficult to get comparable information about man from human clinical material. As is clear from Doty's experiment, such studies require geometrical types of surgical section within the brain, and such experimental lesions have no counterpart in any neurological disease. Still, there would be no reason at all to think that such a basic matter as the plan of functional interconnection between different parts of the brain would have changed substantially from cat to man.

The newer interest in neural structures located at many levels of the brain, along with evidences of widespread inter-action between anatomically higher and lower centers, has in-fluenced the way investigators interpret the results of behav-ioral studies of brain function. Nowadays it is understood that, if a lesion in some particular part of the brain leads to some behavioral deficit, this fact means only that the dam-aged brain tissue is part of some neural circuit (potentially involving structures at many levels of the brain) that needs to be intact for the normal function of the ability under study. Such a conclusion is quite different from saying that the brain area in question must have controlled the ability or have been responsible for it or, even worse, that the ability must have been localized exclusively in that particular part of the brain —as if there were many faculties each having its own special seat in the brain, in the way the phrenologists believed a cen-tury and a half ago and the psychophysiologists considered reasonable earlier in this century. For example, the fact that a person is blind following total destruction of his visual cortex certainly does not mean that the visual function is in any ex-clusive way localized there. It does mean that neural circuits or pathways that connect with cells in this particular cortical area are essential for the entire sense of sight in man. What in particular is contributed to vision by the cortex or by lower visual centers in the subcortex can only be decided by sepa-rate experiments, each specifically directed toward answering these various questions.

The same kind of caution is necessary in drawing anatomical conclusions from behavioral experiments that involve electrical or chemical stimulation of particular brain structures. Such artificial activation initiates changes that can spread along nerve pathways and the critical effect, so far as some particular sample of behavior is concerned, could well lie in a neural structure quite remote from the location of the stimulating electrode or stimulating chemical. The same discretion is also necessary when one attempts to correlate recorded electrical activity in a particular brain structure with some type of observed behavior. It is always possible that the recorded activity is only a byproduct of more crucial electrical events elsewhere in the brain.

These are some of the principles that must be kept in mind in considering the neurology of behavior. There are, nevertheless, frequent occasions when knowledge is still insufficient to permit an accurate description of how a particular center is functionally related to other parts of the brain. For this reason it is often convenient to discuss a particular part of the brain in isolation, as though that part were capable of influencing behavior without involving other pathways or centers at all. Such a manner of speaking, as should now be clear, is only a useful fiction.

2

THE ANATOMY OF SELECTED SUBCORTICAL STRUCTURES

THE NERVOUS SYSTEM of vertebrate animals, including man, has two main parts. The *central nervous system* is made up of the brain and spinal cord, and the *peripheral nervous system* includes all the nerves that extend throughout the body. Both the central and the peripheral parts of the system can be further subdivided in a number of ways, important among them being the basic subdivision into *somatic* and *autonomic* components. The somatic nervous system, as it is sometimes called, controls our movements and evaluates changes in our *external environment*. The autonomic nervous system is concerned only with handling physiological processes inside the body or, as it is also known, the *internal environment*.

Somatic nerves either activate the muscles of the limbs and trunk (*somatomotor nerves*) or they carry sensory information from the peripheral receptors, or sense organs, back to the central nervous system (*somatosensory nerves*). Autonomic nerves also are either sensory or motor, carrying information about the state of affairs in the internal environment back to the brain or initiating physiological changes somewhere in the body. It is the autonomic nerves that connect the brain and spinal cord with the visceral organs such as the heart, lungs, intestines, and sexual organs. Various parts of the autonomic nervous system are considered either *sympathetic* or *parasympathetic,* depending on the kind of physiological processes for which they are responsible. We shall consider this last distinction more carefully later, but, simply put, the sympathetic system is most active when an organism is alertly engaged or working strenuously, while the parasympathetic system has the primary responsibility of attending to the body's "housekeeping chores"—controlling, for instance, the digestive processes. This distinction is actually one of emphasis, however, since both these parts of the autonomic system are to some extent constantly active.

When sensory information reaches the central nervous system via the sensory nerves, it is integrated and correlated with other information stored in the brain, and messages signaling appropriate action are sent via the motor nerves to the muscles and viscera. This continuous coordination by the nervous system is what permits animals—including man—to behave adaptively in response to changes in the external environment as well as to changes in their own internal environment. As we shall see, subcortical systems are concerned with the organism's adaptation to both these types of change.

The nervous system, like other tissues of the body, is made up of cells. There are two main types of cell in nervous tissue. The *neuron* or nerve cell is responsible for transmitting the electrical nerve impulse which is the basic unit of neural activity. The second type of cell in the brain is the *glial cell,* which provides metabolic and mechanical support for the nerve cells.

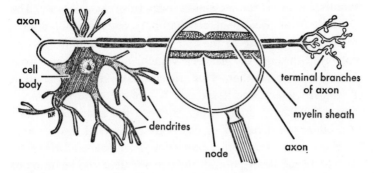

FIGURE 2–1. Diagram of a nerve cell or neuron. At the left is the cell body, with its centrally located nucleus and numerous branching dendrites. The nerve fiber or axon can run for a short or long distance and in any direction from the cell body. Above it is shown arching to the right and is drawn, for diagrammatic purposes, as though split lengthwise. The magnified portion of the split nerve fiber shows the axon, its covering myelin sheath, and an interruption in the sheath known as a node. The terminal branches of the axon, shown at the extreme right, would normally be in contact with the cell bodies or dendrites of other neurons. At these points of contact, known as synapses, the nerve impulse of one neuron can be transmitted to the next nerve cell in line.

All neurons have the same basic structure (see Figure 2–1). Each neuron has a cell body which, as in all cells, is enclosed by a cell membrane and contains cytoplasm and a centrally placed nucleus. Two types of cytoplasmic process project from the nerve-cell body: several *dendrites* which function as spatial extensions of the cell body, and a single *axon* which conducts the electrical nerve impulse away from the cell body and its dendrites. The axon is also known as a *nerve fiber,* and it may have an insulating covering known as a *myelin sheath*. When a myelin sheath is present it is not continuous along the entire nerve fiber but is periodically discontinuous at points referred to as *nodes of Ranvier*. The axon may be short and branching and end in the vicinity of its cell body, or it may be long (as suggested in Figure 2–1) and carry nerve impulses to areas some distance away from the cell body. The dendrites (an occasional cell has only one) usually branch freely and end close to the cell body. Nerve impulses, to be conveyed through the nervous system, must be passed from one neuron to another. This transfer takes place at a point (*synapse*) where one nerve cell is in close contact with another. Synapses usually occur between the axon of one cell and either the dendrites or cell body of the cell next in line.

There are a few terms that should be defined before we turn to a brief description of the development and anatomy of certain subcortical structures. In the first place, a group of nerve fibers (as many as several million) frequently run along together from one place to another in the central nervous system. These collections of fibers are known as *pathways, tracts,* or *bundles.* Similarly, cell bodies within the central nervous system also collect in distinguishable groups having a common appearance and similar connections with other parts of the brain. Such a collection of cells is known as a *nucleus.* Two or more nuclei are said to be connected if tracts run between them, and Figure 2–2 illustrates the special terms used to describe the type and direction of connections between nuclei. The nerve fibers in a tract may provide a *direct pathway* from one nucleus to another, or the pathway may be interrupted by synapses along its course. In the latter case, the tract is called a *polysynaptic pathway.* Furthermore, a tract is said to be *afferent* or *efferent,* depending on the direction in which it carries nerve impulses relative to some point of reference (for example, the nucleus at either end of the tract). An afferent tract carries nerve impulses toward the nucleus of reference while efferent bundles conduct impulses in the opposite direction. Figure 2–2 also shows how an afferent pathway has its cell bodies of origin outside the nucleus of reference, while the cell bodies of efferent tracts are within the nucleus. Finally, one nucleus is said to *project* on another if it sends an efferent tract to the second nucleus. The brain is basically an extremely complex arrangement of nuclei and their connecting tracts.

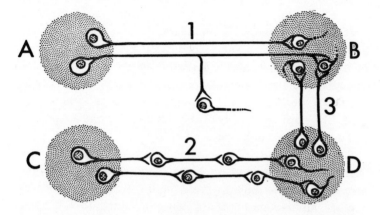

FIGURE 2–2.   A schematic diagram representing nuclei and nerve pathways in the brain. The stippled areas (A, B, C, and D) represent four different clusters of nerve-cell bodies, or nuclei. In each schematic nucleus a few cell bodies are shown, and their axon extensions form three nerve pathways or fiber bundles (1, 2, and 3). Pathways 1 and 3 are *direct pathways* (nonsynaptic). Pathway 2 is made up of many short neurons and synapses and represents a *polysynaptic pathway*. As described more fully in the text, pathways 1, 2, and 3 are, respectively, efferent fiber bundles from nuclei A, C, and D while 1 and 3 are afferent to nuclei B and pathway 2 is afferent to nucleus D. It can also be said that nuclei A and D project on nucleus B while C projects on D. The lower axon or nerve fiber in pathway 1 is sending an offshoot or *collateral* to a cell body outside of the four main nuclei represented.

Embryonic and Phylogenetic Development of the Brain

The structure of the subcortical parts of the brain is most easily understood if we consider some general facts about the development of the adult nervous system from its simple tubular form in the early embryo. The nervous system is formed first by an infolding of the outer layer of the embryo, which thus creates the cylindrical *neural tube* that runs along the back from one end of the embryo to the other. At the head of the embryo, this neural tube enlarges more rapidly than it does toward the tail. This enlarged region, destined to be the brain, develops three subdivisions: an anterior *forebrain*, a *midbrain* behind it, and a *hindbrain* at the rear (see A of Figure 2–3). The remaining part of the neural tube, extending down the back of the embryo, is to become the spinal cord. The cord changes relatively little in later development, and we need not consider it further.

During the course of development, however, many changes occur in the structure of the brain. Nerve cells in the embryonic brain start to multiply more rapidly in one place than in another, and certain groups of neurons migrate to new locations in the brain. At the same time, nerve pathways of various sizes begin to connect the young nuclei that are developing throughout the central nervous system of the embryo. As a consequence of this cellular activity, five secondary subdivisions, which constitute the basic units of the adult brain, arise from the three primary embryonic subdivisions, as can be seen in B of Figure 2–3. To form one of the secondary subdivisions, the lateral walls of the forebrain dilate to make the cerebral hemispheres or *telencephalon*. Behind this, the remaining part of the original forebrain forms a second subdivision called the "between-brain" or *diencephalon*. The diencephalon is continuous posteriorly with the remaining three subdivisions: the *mesencephalon, metencephalon,* and *myelencephalon*. These latter three subdivisions, except for the cerebellum, which develops from the roof of the metencephalon, are sometimes considered together in the adult brain; in this case they are collectively called the *brainstem*.

All five subdivisions in this embryonic brain are subcortical structures, since the neocortex has not yet developed. Only during the later embryonic stages in the higher verte-

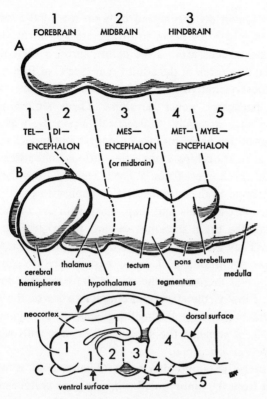

FIGURE 2-3. Embryonic pattern of development for the vertebrate brain. In the very young embryo, the primitive tubular brain (A) first develops three subdivisions. In the course of later embryonic development, these three primary subdivisions further subdivide (B) to form five secondary subdivisions: the telencephalon, the diencephalon, the mesencephalon, the metencephalon, and the myelencephalon. Also indicated in B are the areas within these subdivisions where major components of the adult nervous system will further differentiate during subsequent embryonic development. Diagram C, a medial view of the cat brain which has been split lengthwise between the two cerebral hemispheres, shows how the five secondary subdivisions come to be distributed in the adult vertebrate brain. In higher vertebrates, such as the cat, a layer of neocortex is also present as the outer shell of the adult telencephalon, covering the more primitive cerebral hemispheres as they are seen in the embryo (see text). Also shown in C is the brain surface, which was originally the top of the embryonic brain and is known as the dorsal surface. The underside of the brain is referred to as its ventral surface.

brates and man do specialized cells on top of the primitive cerebral hemispheres begin to proliferate and form an outer shell of nerve cells around the hemispheres, a shell that becomes the neocortex of the adult brain (see C of Figure 2–3). In the most primitive vertebrate animals, fish and amphibians, a neocortex never develops. These simple animals therefore have a totally "subcortical" brain even as adults. Such a primitive brain provides a convenient model in which to see the relationships among the various subcortical structures in their simplest form. What is learned from the primitive vertebrate brain, moreover, also applies to the brains of more complex animals and man, since with evolutionary development the brain does not discard its original structural patterns. They are merely modified and expanded in keeping with later evolutionary changes, particularly in connection with the great increase in the size of the neocortex in higher animals. Finally, the structural characteristics of the simpler vertebrate brain suggest something about the original functional role of some of the subcortical centers with which we are at present concerned.

The primitive amphibian brain (Figure 2–4) is not very different from the embryonic brain of higher vertebrates. The same five subdivisions are clearly evident. The small cerebral hemispheres receive many direct connections from the olfactory nerve and are almost entirely concerned with the sense of smell. As already noted, no neocortex is present. In the medial walls of these two hemispheres are the *septum* and the *hippocampal area,* the forerunners of two important subcortical structures that are more conspicuous in higher animals. These structures are under the direct domination of the olfactory mechanism in amphibia, but they lose such connections during evolutionary development and, as we shall see, they come to be more closely connected with the diencephalon and the neocortex. All the structures present in these amphibian

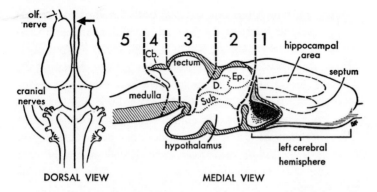

FIGURE 2–4. Dorsal and medial view of the brain of an amphibian, the tiger salamander. The straight vertical line in the dorsal view indicates the plane in which the brain was cut to provide the medial view of the brain when it is observed from the direction indicated by the arrow at the top of the dorsal diagram. The broken line in the diagram indicates the level of division between the thalamus and the tectum. The diagonally hatched areas in the medial diagram indicate the cut surfaces that resulted from the midline sectioning of the intact brain. The numbered areas divided by broken lines in the medial view are anatomically similar to the five subdivisions of the embryonic brain of higher vertebrates (see B of Figure 2–3). Cb. = cerebellum; D. = dorsal thalamus; Ep. = epithalamus; olf. nerve = olfactory nerve; Sub. = subthalamus. (Based on material from C. J. Herrick, *The Brain of the Tiger Salamander, Amblystoma Tigrinum*. Chicago: University of Chicago Press, 1948.)

hemispheres, however, are still present within the cerebral hemispheres of the higher animals. They are then called the *rhinencephalon* (*rhine* means nose) because of their earlier more intimate connection with the sense of smell. The reduction of direct olfactory connections and the development of the neocortex are the two most important features of the phylogenetic development of the cerebral hemispheres.

The diencephalon in the primitive amphibia still retains the embryonic shape of a tube of tissue surrounding the cavity of the third ventricle. The walls of this tube consist of four longitudinally arranged zones of cells which, taken together, make up the *thalamlus* (see Figure 2–4). The uppermost zone is the *epithalamus,* which has connections both forward to the telencephalon and back to the brainstem. Below the epithalamus is the *dorsal thalamus,* which is quite small in amphibia. This dorsal part of the thalamus expands greatly in mammals, however, since a number of nuclei form here that provide important upward connections to the expanding neocortex of higher animals. The dorsal thalamus becomes the largest part of the thalamus in mammals. Immediately below the dorsal thalamus is the *subthalamus;* the zone of cells at the bottom of the thalamus is called the *hypothalamus.* The hypothalamus has extensive connections with other parts of the brain; as we shall see later, investigators have discovered a great deal about its contributions to behavior.

In the amphibia as well as in all other vertebrates, the remainder of the brain, below the thalamus and above the spinal cord, consists in the various components of the brainstem. The brainstem contains all of the nuclei that give rise to the cranial nerves and all of the motor and sensory tracts that run back and forth between the higher brain centers and the spinal cord. Recent experiments suggest that these nuclei in the brainstem connected with the cranial nerves are more than relay nuclei that simply pass information into or out of the central nervous system. These nuclei apparently perform some integrative functions that can modify the sensory or motor processes with which they are concerned.

The general plan of the brainstem in all vertebrates is quite simple. The dorsal part (with the exception of the cerebellum) is concerned mainly with sensory input to the brain, and the ventral part, with motor or response processes. Between these sensory and motor zones is a core of more complex structure and function, the *reticular formation.* In primitive vertebrates such as the amphibia, scientists believe that the reticular formation is a major integrating center for both motor and sensory processes. In higher animals, however, there is an increased sharing of some of these complex functions by

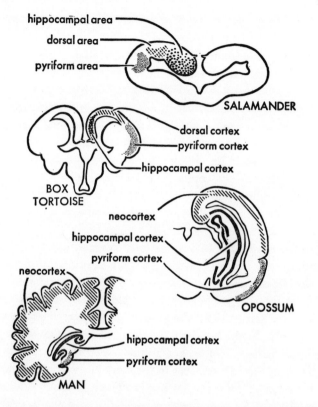

FIGURE 2–5. Diagrammatic cross-sections through the hemispheres of representative vertebrates showing the manner in which the neocortex expands throughout the vertebrate series at the expense of more primitive structures in the telencephalon, such as the hippocampal and the pyriform cortex. In the salamander, the forerunners of all of these structures are present, although their function is thought to be entirely olfactory. In the more advanced tortoise, the situation is much the same, although the dorsal cortex is more differentiated and thus begins to take on some of the characteristics of the neocortex of higher vertebrates. In the opossum, an early mammal, a neocortex is plainly evident, but it does not yet equal in size the combined extent of the hippocampal and the pyriform cortex. In higher mammals, as shown above for man, the neocortex comes to occupy a larger and larger proportion of the cerebral hemispheres; the pyriform cortex is, then, the only cortical zone remaining under direct olfactory domination. (Modified from C. J. Herrick, "The functions of the olfactory parts of the cerebral cortex." *Proceedings of the National Academy of Sciences,* 1933, **19**, 7–14; reprinted with permission of the publisher.)

higher brain centers as a result of the later evolutionary changes already mentioned.

During evolutionary development, the higher brain centers do not simply take over the behavioral functions that were originally the responsibility of lower subcortical centers. For example, as the neocortex grows in size and complexity in higher animals (see Figure 2–5), it supplies new functional capabilities and comes to have an important influence on the more primitive brain circuits that continue to operate, however, in the lower centers. The functions of all subcortical regions remain essential to the actions of the brain, but they come to be substantially influenced by activity in the neocortex.

In the pages that follow, we shall concentrate on the contributions to behavior made by three major subcortical regions: the ascending reticular system, the hypothalamus, and parts of the rhinencephalon. Of all the subcortical structures, behavioral scientists have studied these three regions the most intensively. Since we shall be concerned for the most part with the behavior of higher animals, Figure 2–6 shows the location of these three areas in the adult brain of a representative mammal, the cat. Their placement is quite similar in man. Except for the conspicuous addition of the neocortex, the general organization of the brain of the cat, and man as well, is basically similar to what is found in the amphibia.

The Reticular Formation

The reticular formation is a core of tissue which runs centrally through the entire brainstem, as indicated in Figure 2–6. It is surrounded by ascending and descending tracts as well as by the motor and sensory nuclei of the cranial nerves. Posteriorly, the reticular formation is continuous with the cell

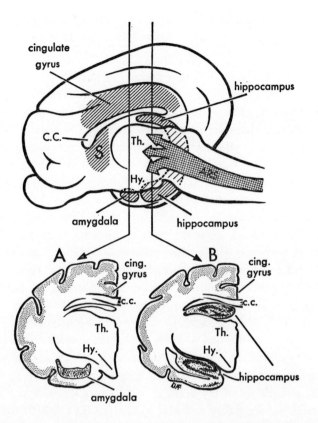

FIGURE 2–6. Diagrams of the cat brain to show the location of the ascending reticular formation, the hypothalamus and some of the major structures in the rhinencephalon. At the top is a medial view of the brain after it has been split lengthwise between the two cerebral hemispheres. It can be compared directly with C of Figure 2–3 and is also the same view as that of the amphibian brain shown in Figure 2–4. Diagrams A and B are cross-sections through the half-brain shown at the levels indicated by the vertical lines in the top drawing. The cross-hatched area represents the approximate position of the ascending reticular formation (ARS) as it extends upward through the brainstem. The diagonally hatched areas represent the major rhinencephalic structures that make up the limbic lobe. While the cingulate gyrus and the septal area (S) are midline structures, the hippocampus and amygdala are located deeper inside the cerebral hemisphere, as shown in A and B. ARS = ascending reticular system; c.c. = corpus callosum (a heavy elongated fiber bundle that runs between the two cerebral hemispheres); cing. gyrus = cingulate gyrus; Hy. = hypothalamus; S = septal area; Th. = thalamus.

bodies that make up the core of the spinal cord and extends anteriorly into the hypothalamus and the central part of the thalamus. The term reticular formation describes the microscopic appearance of this region when thin cross-sections of the brainstem are stained so that the nerve fibers can be seen. In such material, interlacing nerve fibers can be seen running helter-skelter in all directions throughout the reticular formation, making a weblike network or *reticulum* of fibers in which the cell bodies of neurons are diffusely embedded.

A trained neuroanatomist can discern a number of discrete subdivisions within the reticular formation. Physiological and behavioral studies, however, have so far uncovered only two general systems within this brainstem structure to which different functions can be broadly ascribed. First, there is a *descending reticular system,* capable of modifying the electrical activity in nerve cells throughout the lower brainstem and spinal cord. This descending system can both facilitate and inhibit the transmission of nerve impulses in both sensory and motor systems. Its most persistent effect, under normal circumstances, seems to be that of suppressing or damping the input and output of the brain at these lower levels. Secondly, there is an *ascending reticular system* (ARS), which maintains the proper level of electrical activity in many of the higher brain centers, in particular the neocortex. It is this ascending system that has recently captured the interest of behavioral scientists, and the following anatomical description will thus be limited to it.

One of the most striking characteristics of the reticular formation is the great number of sensory fibers that feed into it. Nerve fibers from all of the sensory systems transmit nerve impulses to the ARS (see Figure 2–7). Afferent pathways from receptors in the skin and muscles arrive in the ARS either by tracts ascending from the spinal cord or by offshoots (*collaterals*) from sensory axons destined to connect higher

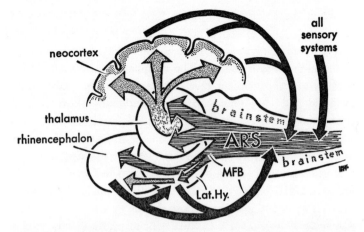

FIGURE 2–7. Highly schematic diagram of the major connections to and from the ascending reticular system (ARS). As also indicated in Figure 2–6, the ARS ascends in the core of the brainstem. It makes connections with cell bodies in the thalamus and the lateral hypothalamus, as well as sending some fibers through the lateral hypothalamus directly into various structures in the rhinencephalon. As shown by the stippled arrows, some parts of the thalamus in turn diffuse the influence of the ARS over the neocortex while some cells in the lateral hypothalamus send fibers into rhinencephalic structures for the same purpose. Shown schematically by the arrows are the three major sources of sensory input to the ARS: from all the sensory systems of the body, from the neocortex, and from the rhinencephalon. The fibers of the ventral portion of this system (interconnecting the ARS, the lateral hypothalamus, and the rhinencephalon) are carried in the important medial forebrain bundle. ARS = ascending reticular system; Lat. Hy. = lateral hypothalamus; MFB = medial forebrain bundle.

up in the brain. Nerve fibers from subcortical nuclei receiving other sensory information (e.g., visual and auditory) also send collaterals to the reticular formation. These sensory axons mostly arrive in the lateral areas of the reticular formation where they form synapses with short neurons that conduct the sensory nerve impulses to the medial portion of the reticular formation. The ARS also receives afferent fibers from the neocortex and from various structures in the rhinencephalon (see Figure 2–7).

When these sensory impulses feed into the ARS, they increase its level of electrical activity. The ARS in turn transmits this *activation,* or *arousal* as it is commonly called, to many of the higher brain centers. The pathways that transmit these sensory effects to higher levels of the brain are mostly polysynaptic pathways made up of a great many short neurons connected in series. Some of the ARS tracts, however, are composed of longer axons and only a few synapses. In the midbrain, the pathways of the ARS diverge to form two separate groups of ascending fibers. As shown in Figure 2–7, one group travels dorsally to enter the thalamus and the other projects ventrally into the hypothalamus by way of the *medial forebrain bundle* (MFB). This ventral pathway has an important influence on the hypothalamus and, in addition, some of its fibers continue on through the hypothalamus to enter nearby structures at the base of the cerebral hemispheres in the rhinencephalon. Many of the hypothalamic cells that receive axons from the reticular formation also send their axons in turn into the rhinencephalon. This ventral ARS pathway apparently exerts considerable control over the level of neural activity in both hypothalamus and rhinencephalon. The dorsal ARS pathway is thought to project upward through the subthalamus and dorsal thalamus. From the thalamus, the influence of the ARS spreads diffusely over the entire neocortex (see Figure 2–7). The exact manner in which this dorsal pathway reaches the neocortex is unknown. Neuroanatomists do know, however, that the pathways of the reticular system do not form synapses in the specific sensory nuclei of the thalamus, like the *lateral geniculate* for vision or the *medial geniculate* for hearing. As will be described in Chapter 4, this diffuse projection to the neocortex provides the anatomical basis by which the ARS is able to exert generalized control over neocortical activity. For example, whether or not the ARS is maintaining a high enough level of arousal in the neocortex helps to determine whether you are awake or asleep.

The Hypothalamus

The hypothalamus is the most ventral part of the thalamus. This subcortical center is continuous with the base of the cerebral hemispheres in the front, and posteriorly merges into the underside of the midbrain, as figures 2–3 and 2–6 illustrate. There are two rather distinct zones throughout the length of the hypothalamus. The *medial hypothalamic area* is packed with cell bodies and closely surrounds the cavity of the third ventricle, which runs through the middle of the hypothalamus. On both sides of the medial area are the lateral hypothalamic zones (see Figure 2–8), containing the fibers of the medial forebrain bundle (MFB). This important bundle of fibers originates mainly in the rhinencephalon, farther forward in the brain, and runs back through the entire length of the lateral hypothalamus. The medial forebrain bundle, however, contains both ascending and descending fiber pathways. Some of the fibers of the MFB that originate in the rhinencephalon pass through the hypothalamus and enter the reticular formation, but most of them terminate on cells in the lateral hypothalamus. Similarly, most ascending fibers of the MFB arise in the reticular formation and form synapses with lateral hypothalamic cells, although a few continue forward into the rhinencephalon. Nerve cells in the lateral hypothalamic zone either send their axons directly into the medial hypothalamus or they ascend or descend in the medial forebrain bundle. This bundle is therefore an important pathway for hypothalamic connections between the reticular formation in the brainstem and the rhinencephalon farther forward in

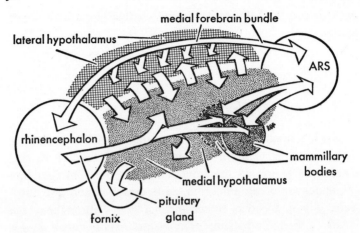

FIGURE 2–8.   Schematic diagram showing the major connections of
the lateral and medial portions of the hypothalamus. The medial forebrain bundle interconnects the ascending reticular system (ARS), the
lateral hypothalamus and the rhinencephalon (as also shown in Figure
2–7). The medial hypothalamus, particularly the mammillary bodies
included within it, also has two-way connections with the ARS and
receives a major afferent bundle (the fornix) from the hippocampus,
forward in the rhinencephalon. The medial hypothalamus also contains
cells that send efferent fibers into the pituitary gland that is attached
to the ventral surface of the hypothalamus. Also represented are the
many short axons that pass back and forth between the lateral and
medial zones of the hypothalamus.

the cerebral hemispheres. The lateral hypothalamic zone is
thought to serve as an important intermediary between these
regions and the medial hypothalamus.

The medial hypothalamus also has fiber connections with a
number of subcortical regions other than the lateral hypothalamus. As shown in Figure 2–8, the medial hypothalamus is
connected directly with the reticular formation and the rhinencephalon. Parts of the medial hypothalamus, near the
place where the stalk of the pituitary gland is attached, also
send important connections to this structure, which in turn
controls the body's system of endocrine glands. Finally, the
medially placed pair of *mammillary bodies* are located at the

posterior border of the medial hypothalamus. These conspicuous nuclei receive a large bundle of fibers (the *fornix*
bundle) from the hippocampus, which is forward in the rhinencephalon, and they are also directly interconnected with
the ARS. In addition to these neural connections (illustrated
in Figure 2–8), the mammillary bodies send an efferent pathway forward and dorsally to the *anterior thalamus*. As described more fully below, the pathway which runs from the
rhinencephalon back to the mammillary bodies and then
forward again to the anterior thalamus is one link in a famous neural circuit (*Papez' circuit*), first described in 1937
by the anatomist James W. Papez.

The Rhinencephalon

The rhinencephalon is composed of two separate groups of
structures. One group contains the olfactory bulbs, from
which the olfactory nerves arise, and the olfactory nuclei, to
which the sensory nerves for smell project. The second group
of structures in the rhinencephalon make up the *limbic lobe,*
which develops in close association with the olfactory areas;
in the course of evolution, however, the centers in the limbic
lobe lose their direct connection with the receptors for the
sense of smell. These limbic structures are the *septal area,* the
cingulate gyrus, the *entorhinal cortex,* the *hippocampus,* and
the major part of the *amygdala.* The term "limbic" (*limbus*
means edge, perimeter) is applied to these structures because,
taken together, they form an annular pattern or ring on the
medial surface of the cerebral hemisphere around the area
where it connects with the diencephalon (see Figure 2–6).
The limbic lobe is interposed between three sets of neural
influences. It receives input from the group of rhinencephalic

centers that are primarily concerned with the sense of smell,
from the neocortex, and from the hypothalamus and reticular
system. The sensory input to these limbic structures is not at
all limited to olfaction, although the pathways from the other
senses are not well understood. Some sensory input probably
reaches the limbic structures through the reticular formation;
in addition, some reports indicate that afferent information
can also reach the rhinencephalon over tracts that project
down from sensory areas of the neocortex. These centers
in the limbic lobe also send different fibers up to the neocortex and, as shown in figures 2–7 and 2–8, down to the
hypothalamus and the reticular formation.

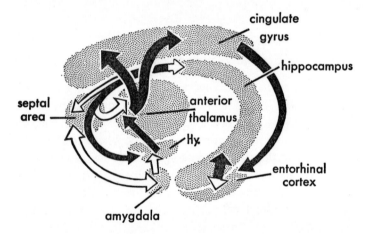

FIGURE 2–9. Schematic diagram showing the neural structures included in the limbic system and their interconnecting fiber pathways.
The seven stippled areas represent the separate structures which are
arranged in a manner that approximately matches their relative position in the intact vertebrate brain (see Figure 2–6). The arrows show
the direction of the control effected by the connecting pathways;
double-ended arrows indicate that connecting fibers have effects in
both directions. The outflow from the hippocampus is the fornix
bundle (also see Figure 2–8). The closed circuit represented by the
black arrows is Papez' circuit. Within the thalamus proper, only the
anterior portion is considered part of the limbic system. Hy. = hypothalamus.

The various structures in the limbic lobe are closely connected with one another as well as with other parts of the brain (see Figure 2–9). The anterior thalamus and the hypothalamus also appear in Figure 2–9, since these structures in the diencephalon, taken together with the limbic portion of the rhinencephalon, make up the so-called *limbic system* (see Chapter 5). The connections within the limbic system (diagrammed in Figure 2–9) include the famous Papez' circuit. The fiber pathways of this circuit form a closed loop, running from the hippocampus to the hypothalamus (mammillary bodies), from the hypothalamus to the anterior thalamus, and from the thalamus back to the hippocampus by way of the cingulate gyrus and the entorhinal cortex. Papez' suggestion that activity in this circuit might provide the neural basis of emotional experience has been responsible for a great deal of behavioral research (see Chapter 5).

3

THE HYPOTHALAMUS AND CONSUMMATORY BEHAVIOR

LONG BEFORE the relatively recent growth of interest in the role of subcortical centers in more complex behavior, scientists were well aware that the hypothalamus contributes to the regulation of the *consummatory behavior* prompted by the biological need for food, water, and a mate. (Consummatory is from *consummare,* to consummate, to achieve—not from *consumere,* to consume, to make away with.) Over the years anatomists, physiologists, and psychologists have applied their research skills to the study of this tiny subcortical area. For the hypothalamus, however, as with every other part of the brain, what the scientist still wishes to learn exceeds the knowledge he presently has. Nevertheless, as we shall see, the study of the function of this brain structure has yielded a great number of experimental findings that can be fitted into a consistent if not final pattern. First we shall consider the general physiological characteristics of the hypothalamus and then see how its experimental manipulation influences the consummatory responses—eating, drinking and mating—associated with the respective biological drives.

At first it seems surprising that so small an area in the central nervous system can play so critical a role in the control of so many vital processes, but the hypothalamus has, as it were, excellent connections. As we saw in the preceding chapter, it is connected with the rhinencephalon in the forebrain; there are, moreover, important pathways from the forebrain that pass through the hypothalamus on their way to structures lower down in the brainstem. The hypothalamus is also richly innervated by a variety of sensory fibers. It furthermore has connections with other important structures in the brainstem, particularly the reticular system. Finally, the *pituitary gland,* the so-called master gland of the endocrine system, is attached directly to the undersurface of the hypothalamus and is influenced by hypothalamic activity.

Many of the types of behavior clearly influenced by experimental manipulations of the hypothalamus, like drinking and eating, involve simple responses in which changes are relatively easy to measure. Earlier workers were thus able to detect more easily some of the contributions of the hypothalamus to behavior, while the secrets of many other subcortical structures concerned with more complex types of behavior are only slowly being deciphered. When our knowledge of other areas in the brain has drawn abreast of our knowledge of the hypothalamus, it may no longer appear that this little diencephalic structure bears so disproportionately large a share of responsibility for the well-being of the animal.

Although it is the more primitive and biological types of behavior that are most clearly associated with hypothalamic function, there is much to be learned about brain function in general from an understanding of the mechanisms through which the hypothalamus influences behavior. For example, in considering all that is involved in the regulation of eating, drinking, and mating, we shall see that the hypothalamus, in order to do its job, must influence general metabolic activities in organs throughout the body and in turn be sensitive also to the metabolic needs of the body at any particular instant. It must modify chemical reactions throughout the body and also react when necessary to the outcome of such chemical reactions, even when they are being influenced by circumstances outside the central nervous system. Similarly, the hypothalamus controls the secretion of many hormones, the biologically active chemical compounds secreted by the widely distributed endocrine glands. At the same time, it must react appropriately to changes in the amounts of these hormones in the circulating blood with which it is plentifully supplied. Further, the hypothalamus, in order to regulate consummatory behavior sensibly, must take into account sensory information from both the external and internal environments.

To add to the complexity of the scientific problem, the behavior of organisms that are endeavoring simply to eat, drink, or perpetuate their species is influenced not only by basic physiological factors but by their past experiences as well. An animal, for instance, will not eat in a place where it has just received an electric shock. The brain clearly contains mechanisms whereby psychological processes more complex than an animal's biological needs can influence appetitive behavior. Similarly, and perhaps most puzzling of all, the responses of an animal under the influence of one of the biological drives can vary from such stereotyped, reflexive acts as sniffing, chewing, and swallowing to such goal-oriented and nonstereotyped movements as avoiding inedible materials, fighting an adversary for control of a source of water, or seeking one mate in preference to others. It is possible to describe nerve pathways that might connect the hypothalamic "hunger center" to the nerve cells that control the muscles for chewing, but it is far more difficult—seemingly impossible at the present time—to imagine how the "hunger center" of an animal deprived of food influences the leg muscles in a manner that permits a hungry animal to search successfully for food in a strange environment. Many of the general mysteries of how the nervous system mediates any kind of behavior could be answered by a full understanding of how the hypothalamus helps regulate the great variety of behavior patterns, simple and complex, associated with the biological drives.

Activity in the hypothalamus, even in the simplest case, only could lead to an adaptive consummatory response by influencing both metabolic systems and sets of muscle fibers such as are used, for instance, in chewing and swallowing. To understand how the hypothalamus does its job, therefore, one must know how it manages to control the needed response systems. Similarly, on the sensory side, it is not enough to know that some particular part in the hypothalamus of a hungry or thirsty animal becomes active; one must know precisely how such metabolic needs of the body are signaled to the hypothalamus. To say simply that there is a "hunger center" which becomes active and, in turn, initiates eating is a starting point, but it is of little more final scientific value than to state the well-known fact that a hungry animal, given food, will eat. The goal is to understand how the physiological functions of a particular part of the brain, along with its afferent and efferent connections, account for the particular role it plays in behavior.

Investigators use complicated and varied techniques to study the physiological functions of particular parts of the central nervous system such as the hypothalamus. These experimental techniques are tailored, of course, to the particular physiological system under study, but for present purposes they can be grouped into half a dozen general categories. For example, using electrical techniques, physiologists stimulate

parts of the brain in anesthetized animals through a wire electrode buried there and look for physiological changes elsewhere in the body. They can measure associated changes in
blood pressure, in general metabolic rate, or in the secretion
of a particular hormone, to mention but a few of the associated events. Using surgical techniques, investigators can damage some part of the brain or cut some of its connections and
make similar measurements, looking this time for physiological abnormalities. Conversely, a physiologist may produce a
peripheral change in the body (e.g., he may inject a hormone
or stimulate a peripheral sensory nerve) and then he will look
for associated electrical changes in the part of the brain he is
studying.

Not only can experimental workers stimulate brain areas
electrically, but they also can use chemical compounds for
the same purpose. They can either start or stop activity in a
nucleus in the nervous system with some biochemical substance, for instance, a neurally active hormone. They then
measure related physiological changes elsewhere in the body
as they do when they stimulate the brain electrically. They can
stimulate the brain chemically either by injecting minute
quantities of the substance directly into a brain center
through a buried *micropipette* or by injecting the chemical
compound into the circulating blood and letting it reach the
brain through its normal blood supply. More recently, investigators have started measuring specific chemical changes
produced in the brain itself by various experimental manipulations elsewhere in the central nervous system or by physiological changes throughout the body.

Behavioral scientists use many of these same procedures to
study the functioning of the brain in behavior, but they do not
ordinarily study anesthetized animals, as physiologists usually
must do to examine the working of physiological systems inside the body. Experimental animals in behavioral studies are

studied when awake and able to move, when their patterns of behavior can be observed and measured.

Physiological Functions of the Hypothalamus

Using experimental procedures of the kinds just described, physiologists have discovered many body processes that are influenced by activity within the hypothalamus. As we have already seen, such physiological effects are handled through the autonomic portion of the nervous system. The autonomic responses that result from stimulating the hypothalamus are most commonly patterned adjustments involving more than one specific visceral system. Thus the hypothalamus has been characterized as an autonomic or visceral *integrating* center. That it is an integrating center is also suggested by anatomical considerations: the hypothalamus contains no cells of origin for nerve fibers directly capable of influencing such autonomic effectors as the heart and the muscles of the intestine. The hypothalamus is thought to have its effect on autonomic activities through its connections with nerves that arise from cells located elsewhere in the brainstem or in the autonomic portions of the spinal cord. This is an ideal arrangement for a center that must activate many autonomic motor nerves in a patterned sequence, and there are known to be descending pathways, originating in the hypothalamus or passing through it, that could provide possible outgoing paths for this physiological purpose.

A list of the autonomic responses that can be influenced by hypothalamic activity reads like a tabulation of all the activities under the control of the autonomic nervous system. For

example, activity in the hypothalamus can produce change in
the size of the pupil of the eye, increase in blood sugar, or
alteration in the activity of sweat glands. Electrical stimulation of different parts of the hypothalamus can slow down the
heart rate or speed it up, increase or decrease blood pressure,
dilate or constrict blood vessels, and excite or suppress movements of the intestine or of other organs inside the body. That
stimulation of the hypothalamus can produce these opposite
effects in the same physiological systems indicates that the
hypothalamus can operate through both the *sympathetic* and
parasympathetic divisions of the autonomic nervous system.

Walter R. Hess, a Swiss physiologist who for many years
studied the function of subcortical systems in his Zürich laboratory, emphasized the fact that the hypothalamus is organized partly with respect to such sympathetic and parasympathetic functions (Hess, 1954). Hess's experiments indicated
that the posterior portion of the hypothalamus, in the area of
the mammillary bodies, is organized as a sympathetic integrating system. He called this portion of the hypothalamus the
ergotrophic zone. Electrical stimulation of this zone produces
such sympathetic responses as acceleration of the heart rate or
an increase of blood pressure. When an investigator implants
electrodes in the brains of cats that are allowed to roam freely
and then electrically stimulates the ergotrophic zone, the cats
exhibit general behavior that seems psychologically to fit with
sympathetic function. They become alert and aroused and,
with continued stimulation, even aggressive. They have been
known to ferociously attack innocuous objects in their environment, even the experimenter's leg. Hess suggested that
this posterior part of the hypothalamus is concerned with
the autonomic support of defensive reactions, such as fighting
or fleeing from an adversary.

In the front of the hypothalamus, in contrast, electrical
stimulation leads to different types of both autonomic and

behavioral response. Hess called this anterior area of the hypothalamus the *tropotrophic zone*. When he electrically stimulated a cat's brain here, he observed responses of a parasympathetic type—the slowing of the heart rate and dilatation of the blood vessels in the stomach and intestine. The cat became calm and drowsy. These responses suggest that the tropotrophic zone is organized to handle vegetative events like digestion and metabolic processes of repair. An animal sluggishly resting while digesting a full meal would be a good example of an organism under the dominant influence of the tropotrophic zone.

These findings emphasize the fact that the hypothalamus is capable of integrating autonomic responses into patterns appropriate to both the metabolic and the psychological circumstances of the moment. It will become clear that the sensitivity of the hypothalamus to changes in the internal environment as well as to changes in the external environment is important for its regulation of the behavior associated with biological drives.

Parts of the hypothalamus also help maintain a constant body temperature in warm-blooded animals. Complete destruction of the hypothalamus causes a nearly total impairment of the control of the body's temperature in both lower animals and man, and, thereafter, the temperature of the body varies drastically in accordance with changes in the external temperature, much as it does in such "cold-blooded" animals as the fish. Processes affecting the production and conservation of heat (e.g., increased metabolic rate and constriction of superficial blood vessels) take place in the posterior hypothalamus. The anterior hypothalamus, on the other hand, contains neural structures that are involved in physiological processes associated with the loss of heat (as dilation of superficial blood vessels and panting). Normally, of course, these opposing systems must be coordinated with each other and responsive to the temperature throughout the rest of the body and to sensory information that comes from temperature receptors in the skin.

Important links in this integrating mechanism for heat control are special nerve cells in the hypothalamus (*thermoreceptors*) which are activated by changes of temperature in the brain tissue around them. The presence of such thermoreceptors has been demonstrated dramatically by studies in which a tiny diathermic unit is buried directly in the anterior hypothalamus of dogs. Through such a unit an investigator can first heat this part of the hypothalamus artificially and then allow it to cool below normal body temperature. In response to these two temperature changes in the hypothalamus the dog first pants and stretches out restfully as if trying to lose heat then becomes active and shivers, increasing heat production. All the time, of course, the dog, whether panting or shivering, is living in the ordinarily comfortable 70°F. temperature of the laboratory. Normally, the temperature of the hypothalamus is determined by the temperature of the circulating blood, which in turn varies with the general body temperature of the animal.

Both Hess's findings and what is known about hypothalamic control of body temperature fit together well; they both indicate some division of function between the front and the back of the hypothalamus. An alerted animal, producing and conserving heat (energy), is functioning properly under the influence of the ergotrophic zone. During tropotrophic conditions, however, a resting well-fed organism can afford the physiological luxury of losing body heat, so valuable at other times, when optimal metabolic requirements call for such an adjustment. The role played by the hypothalamus in controlling the ingestion of food and fluid (see p. 55) and its influence on the production and loss of heat suggest that, in general, the hypothalamus helps to monitor and modify adaptively the exchange of energy between the organism and its environment.

The hypothalamus also has an important functional link with the pituitary gland. It is known to influence the secretion of pituitary hormones by at least two different means. One involves a direct neural connection between the anterior hypothalamus and the posterior lobe of the pituitary. Secondly, however, the hormones previously thought to be synthesized solely by the posterior pituitary can be produced as well by nerve cells located in certain hypothalamic nuclei. These hormones then travel within the axons of these nerve cells to the posterior pituitary gland, where they are either stored or released. This process is called *neurosecretion*. Endocrinologists believe, for instance, that the antidiuretic hormone (ADH), which helps control water loss through the kidney, is a hormone which can be produced by cells in the hypothalamus.

A similar but less well-understood mechanism also appears to regulate secretion of hormones from the anterior lobe of the pituitary. This anterior part of the gland contains few if any nerve fibers. It does, however, have an unusual blood supply which passes down to it from the hypothalamus. Current belief is that some hypothalamic areas produce minute quantities of active compounds that are carried by these special blood vessels to the pituitary, where they selectively activate particular groups of cells in the anterior lobe, leading to the release of particular pituitary hormones. This function of hypothalamic cells can also be considered a type of neurosecretory activity. Such activity is not limited to hypothalamic cells, however, since it is now recognized that most nerve cells are capable of secreting tiny amounts of so-called *neurotransmitters* at the endings of their axons. It is thought to be in this way that axons initiate nerve impulses in the adjacent neurons with which they are in synaptic contact. Some of these hormonal influences of the hypothalamus are important for the drinking, eating, and mating behaviors to be discussed later.

Control of Respiration as
a Model for Hypothalamic Function

Many investigators have been interested in the mechanism by which changes in the body's internal environment (reflected, for example, in physical and chemical changes in the blood) are capable of influencing activity within the central nervous system. Sensitivity to such bodily changes is one of the important capabilities of the hypothalamus. The presence of thermoreceptors, for example, has already been described. The hypothalamus, however, is not the only part of the brain in which bloodborne (*humoral*) factors are able to influence the activity of neurons. Another well-recognized example of this kind of action is found in the so-called respiratory center in the medulla, which is not only an interesting subcortical system in itself but also can serve as a model for the less well-understood hypothalamic mechanisms associated with the primary biological drives.

Strictly speaking, the designation of these medullary control mechanisms as "the respiratory center" is no more justified than is the case with so-called centers that modify more complex types of behavior. The neural structures that influence breathing, a relatively simple response, considerably exceed this restricted locus in the medulla. Respiration can be influenced form neocortical levels as well as from the hypothalamus. Further, there is a particularly important area in the brainstem, at the level of the pons, that has a continuous influence on activity in the respiratory cells of the medulla. Nevertheless, the respiratory control system in the medulla can be considered separately, and it presents a parallel to some of the hypothalamic systems discussed later in this chapter. The parallel is not surprising; respiration is as clearly a consummatory response as drinking, eating, and mating. Under conditions of deprivation, the need for air is certainly far more pressing than, for instance, the need for water. The relation between respiration and the other forms of biologically motivated behavior is suggested by the use of the term *air-hunger,* to describe the drive state of an organism that is suffocating.

In the medulla, the two bilaterally paired zones concerned with respiration are ill-defined areas rather than discrete nuclei. The more ventral zones, occupying a position just a few millimeters on either side of the midline, are called the *inspiratory centers* (see Figure 3–1). Through indirect motor connections to the muscles of respiration, neural activity in these centers results in the positive respiratory movement of inspiration—the expansion of the chest cavity by which air is brought into the lungs. Immediately above and to one side of the inspiratory centers are the so-called *expiratory centers*. It is thought that their major function is to stop the activity of the inspiratory centers at appropriate times. When inspiration is thus inhibited and the respiratory muscles thereby relaxed, the natural elasticity of the rib cage collapses the chest cavity, and the relaxed muscular diaphragm at the bottom of the chest cavity rises to its resting position. In this way air is forced out of the lungs; expiration has occurred. The repetition of this sequence of events produces the well-known respiratory cycle as it occurs in its simplest form. One does not have to be a physiologist, however, to think of many circumstances in which this elementary set of neural events is not sufficient to account for respiratory behavior. For instance,

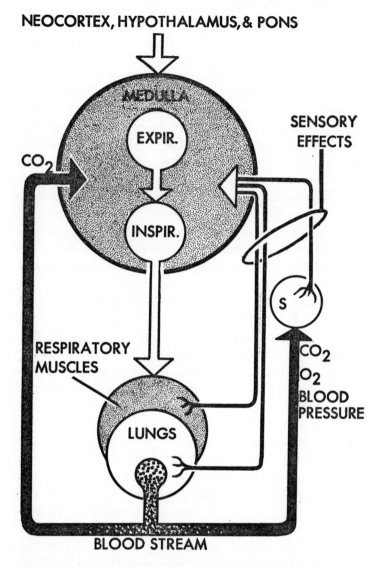

FIGURE 3–1. Schematic diagram showing how the respiratory centers in the medulla are influenced by peripheral respiratory events in the control of breathing. Description in text. Expir. = expiratory center; Inspir. = inspiratory center; S = carotid and aortic sinuses.

you can voluntarily make a forced expiration, as when clearing the nose; you can hold your breath and, with normal respiration temporarily suppressed, whistle a complicated tune while at the same time maintaining an acceptable oxygen balance, and the subtle control of expired air involved in speech is a far cry indeed from the repetitious rhythm of breathing. Still, knowledge of even the simpler respiratory mechanisms involved in normal breathing provides a useful frame of reference for considering the role of the hypothalamus in the control of other types of consummatory behavior that traditionally have been of greater interest to the behavioral scientist.

The respiratory centers are influenced both by the circulating blood and by sensory nerve impulses that reach the medulla through two cranial nerves, the *vagus* nerve and the *glossopharyngeal* nerve. This sensory information arises from receptors buried in the lungs themselves and from specialized sensory structures in the large aortic and carotid arteries. Scientists believe that the inspiratory center is sensitive to changes in the concentration of carbon dioxide in its blood supply but insensitive to changes in the concentration of bloodborne oxygen. An increasing concentration of carbon dioxide in the blood causes an increase of electrical activity, *tonus,* in the inspiratory center. The point to be noted is that a chemical factor in the blood (carbon dioxide) can directly influence the activity of brain cells in much the same way that chemical molecules in the air (for instance, perfume molecules) can produce electrical activity in the receptor cells for smell located high inside the nose. In fact, neurons like those sensitive to carbon dioxide in the inspiratory center are sometimes described as *central receptors.* The details of how such central receptors work is not yet fully known. It is possible, however, to measure slow changes in electrical voltage near such cells when an adequate chemical stimulus is present. These electrical changes might result in the actual firing of nerve impulses, or the slow shifts in voltage might merely lower the central receptor's threshold for being fired off appropriately by other connecting neurons.

The functioning of these respiratory centers in the medulla also is influenced considerably by impulses arriving from outside the central nervous system, as diagrammed in Figure 3–1. Stretch receptors in the lungs, for example, signal the medulla concerning their degree of distention. This sensory mechanism is sensitive to both the amount of lung inflation and the rate at which the inflation is occurring. These incoming nerve impulses, initiated by the act of inspiration, finally activate the expiratory center sufficiently to call into play its inhibitory influence on the inspiratory center, and expiration begins. The exact details of this *Hering-Breuer reflex* are still in question, but the experimental facts as they are now known support best the neural explanation just given. The important fact to remember is that in respiration we have an example of a mechanism of sensory control that is put into play by precisely the response that is being controlled. There are also other sensory systems whereby activity in the respiratory muscles sends sensory information to the medulla and thus influences breathing. Such circular systems of control as these are called *feedback systems,* and it is becoming increasingly clear that they constitute a common form of neural control system operating both within the brain itself and between the brain and various organs of the body.

Another system of control involved in the regulation of the respiratory centers in the medulla deserves brief mention. The aorta and carotid arteries (in the chest and neck, respectively) both contain receptor structures that send afferent nerve fibers to the medulla. In both of these arteries, two types of receptor are present: *pressoreceptors* sensitive to changes of blood pressure and *chemoreceptors* that detect alterations in both the oxygen and the carbon dioxide content of the blood. The chemoreceptors have a more marked effect

on respiration than do the pressoreceptors, and the chemoreceptors of the carotid artery are more important for respiration than are those in the aorta. Stimulation of the carotid
chemoreceptors, for example, whether by decreased oxygen
or by increased carbon dioxide in the circulating blood, influences the respiratory centers in the medulla to increase venti-
lation of the lungs; the depth of breathing is automatically
increased. Just how the sensory input from these carotid receptors modifies the neural centers in the medulla is not yet
known. Possibly the nerve impulses from the carotid receptors induce a higher electrical tonus in the inspiratory center,
an effect similar to that of carbon dioxide when it acts directly on the medulla. These various control systems are sum-
marized in Figure 3–1.

The relatively simple behavior of breathing is thus based
on elaborate supporting mechanisms. It can be influenced by
activity at many different levels of the nervous system, although there is a minimal neural arrangement at the level of
the medulla, which can by itself assure a rhythmic pattern of
respiration compatible with life. Even when one restricts attention to the medulla alone, however, one sees that respiration is regulated by influences of many kinds. There is a patterned interplay between an excitatory (inspiratory) center
and an inhibitory (expiratory) center. The functional relation
between these centers can be influenced directly by the chem-
istry of the medulla's own blood supply or indirectly by humoral factors that stimulate receptors elsewhere in the body.
Moreover, the motor act of respiration itself stimulates still
other receptor cells whose outputs feed back into the medulla
and constitute an additional controlling influence on the
neural activities of the respiratory centers. These control devices are the kind that are frequently seen elsewhere in the
brain, particularly in the hypothalamus, in connection with
more complex forms of behavior.

Humoral Factors Related to
Hunger and Thirst

From what has been said about respiration, it is apparent that the regulation of biological drives by the nervous system is critically influenced by physiological conditions elsewhere in the body. Such metabolic influences as these certainly underlie the hypothalamic control of hunger and thirst, and psychologists and physiologists are still investigating the question of what general bodily changes are responsible for variations in the intensity of these biological drives.

The attempt to answer this question by experiment got under way after 1910 in the Harvard laboratory of Walter B. Cannon, the noted physiologist who was interested in discovering what triggered the behavior of eating and drinking in people and what accounted for their feelings of being hungry or thirsty. In pursuit of this limited set of objectives, Cannon performed a classic series of experiments the results of which pointed to the importance of stomach contractions in producing the pangs of hunger and the dryness of the mouth in thirst, a set of conclusions that came to be known as the "local theory" of biological drives (Cannon, 1934). Later workers extended this local theory to cover the case of sexual motivation, suggesting that irritation or pressure in the genital organs is the peripheral, local factor producing the sex drive. The principle underlying such local theories is that receptor cells in the stomach, mouth, or genitals are stimulated by appropriate physiological changes and the resulting sensory nerve impulses somehow produce activity in the brain that both accounts for the organism's subjective feelings of need and initiates the necessary consummatory response.

It soon became clear that peripheral mechanisms do not

adequately explain all the characteristics of such motivated behavior. For example, a diner goes on to finish his meal after the hunger-contractions of his stomach have ceased early in the meal. The first few swallows of a liquid moisten the mouth quite thoroughly, but the drinker may finish the glassful and have still another. Even more contradictory is the experimental finding that an animal whose stomach has been deprived of its sensory nerves or has even been totally removed is capable of properly regulating its intake of food. Similarly, animals whose mouths are chronically dry because of surgical interference with the salivary glands drink the same amount of water in the course of a day as do normal animals. There is even today no solid experimental evidence for a neural mechanism by which stomach contractions or a dry mouth produce sensory effects in the brain structures concerned with the ingestion of food and water; yet our own personal experience makes it difficult to deny that when we are hungry or thirsty the unpleasant feeling of emptiness in the abdomen or the unpleasant sensation of "cotton" in the dry mouth leads to voluntary eating or drinking that gets rid of the unpleasantness. On the other hand, human experience indicates that vague feelings of need also exist apart from such localized reminders.

After Cannon's time, experimenters began directing their attention to the larger problem of how the body's metabolic requirements control the ingestion of fluid and nourishment. For example, the pioneering psychobiologist Curt Richter began his classic studies that demonstrated that animals can be hungry for specific metabolic materials (Richter, 1942). It seemed clear that stomach contractions and a dry mouth could not be the sole controlling mechanism for consummatory behavior such as this. Slightly later, physiologists demonstrated that the amount an animal drinks is quantitatively related to its water shortage and, moreover, they started to discover some of the body mechanisms that help govern such precise control of fluid intake. Research findings such as these pointed the way for the more recent studies of these problems.

One of the important questions that has concerned investigators is the question of how the organism's need for food or water is mirrored in the blood supply to the brain. In respiration, as we have seen, humoral factors (the blood concentration of carbon dioxide and oxygen) are one of the recognized means by which metabolic states can influence activity in the brain. For thirst, the humoral factors that are best understood at present are the general increase in the concentration of the circulating blood (*hemoconcentration*) and the decreased volume of the circulating blood. Both of these physiological changes occur when an animal is deprived of water; moreover, an otherwise water-satiated animal can be induced to drink by producing either change separately. Drinking can be produced, for instance, by injecting a little concentrated salt solution into the bloodstream, which is one way to produce hemoconcentration. When the hemorrhaging soldier cries for water on the battlefield, it is dramatic evidence of the way in which decreased blood volume can lead to thirst. In the nervous system's regulation of drinking, however, there seems at present no reason to differentiate between these two physiological effects of water deprivation. Hemoconcentration and decreased blood volume have one critical physiological effect in common: both lead to the withdrawal of water from body cells, including nerve cells in the brain. Such *cellular dehydration* in certain hypothalamic cells that are particularly sensitive to water loss, the so-called *osmoreceptors,* appears to be one of the important mechanisms through which metabolic water shortage is signaled to the central nervous system.

How the physiological need for food is signaled to the brain is not yet at all clear. In the first place, food requirements are far more differentiated than is the need for water. Water is water, but, as Richter's early experiments first indicated, animals and people alike are capable of expressing very specific nutritional needs through their eating behavior. Studies show that, given a choice, animals and young children are remarkably successful at choosing dietetically proper proportions of fats, proteins, and carbohydrates. There are also reported cases of children suffering from disorders of the endocrine glands who, for example, are metabolically deficient in salt or calcium. Some of these children, with no advice from parents or doctor, have maintained their health by spontaneously eating extra quantities of salt or making snacks of classroom chalk, which is rich in calcium. The neural control of eating must involve very complex sensing mechanisms. Present-day investigators have yet to explain how the brain manages this remarkable feat.

Even when investigators have restricted their attention to the simpler question of what makes a hungry animal eat at all, they have not yet been able to specify a crucial humoral influence on the brain. A number of such experiments have concentrated on the level of blood sugar (in particular of glucose) but, so far at least, the results indicate that variation in blood glucose alone could not supply the biochemical basis for the neural control of even simple eating behavior. Some reports indicate, however, that when an experimenter observes not just the level of glucose in the circulating blood but, rather, measures the difference between glucose in the arteries and glucose in the veins (thus getting a measure of how much glucose is currently being used inside the body cells), he can make a better prediction about the level of hunger in his experimental subjects. As the difference between the amounts of glucose in the arterial and the venous blood becomes larger, the hunger is reported as greater. These results are not yet conclusive, but they are consistent with other knowledge about the nervous system, since it is changes that alter the inside of brain cells (loss of cellular water, in the case of thirst) that seem capable of influencing the electrical status of neurons and thus of influencing other neural activity and eventually behavior. Whether these particular findings turn out to be the whole truth, there is other evidence to be considered presently which shows that at least one hypothalamic nucleus, known to be involved in the regulation of eating behavior, is particularly sensitive to changes in blood glucose.

Even if glucose does turn out to be in some way involved in signaling the brain about the body's need for more fuel, this single system presumably would not be able to provide a complete physiological basis for what is already known about the various characteristics of eating. Attention has therefore been directed to other additional physiological possibilities. For one thing, other classes of nutrients such as fats and proteins might be involved. Moreover, experiments suggest that changes in heat production in the body, associated with the metabolic use of food, may influence hypothalamic activity in a way that is then reflected in eating behavior. As we have already seen, the hypothalamus is intimately concerned in other ways with the regulation of body temperature. It is also known that the availability of water within certain parts of the internal environment varies both with food deprivation and with the presence or absence of food in the stomach. For example, during and after a meal, when the stomach contains food, body water flows into the stomach cavity to aid in the process of digestion. The result is a temporary, mild dehydration elsewhere in the body. Some think it possible, therefore, that changes in the hydration of hypothalamic cells might contribute something to the regulation of both food and water intake. Indeed, as we shall see, recent research findings show that the hypothalamic mechanisms for controlling eating and drinking are more interconnected than once was thought to be the case.

Hypothalamic Regulation of Eating and Drinking

In 1954, physiological psychologist Eliot Stellar proposed a model for hypothalamic function as it is related to the biological drives. Six years later, in a review of work related to this area, he was able to add a number of new experimental findings (Stellar, 1960), but the model still stands as the best general conceptualization available, based on the research findings currently at hand. Figure 3–2 shows a diagram of this model. As can be seen, the general form of the model has much in common with the description already given of the medullary control of respiration (see Figure 3–1).

As the hub of this schematic conception, Stellar proposed that both inhibitory and excitatory centers exist in the hypothalamus. It was suggested that an excitatory center exists for each of the biological drives. According to this hypothesis, there would be one excitatory center for thirst and another for hunger. Neural activity in such a center would lead to arousal of the relevant drive and culminate in the appropriate consummatory response—drinking in the case of thirst, eating in the case of hunger.

Conversely, the inhibitory center that was postulated for each drive is regarded as a *satiation center*. Neural activity in this type of center would occur when an animal has had enough to eat or drink. The model suggests that a satiation center depresses the level of a drive by inhibiting the related excitatory center. As suggested in Figure 3–2, the effect would

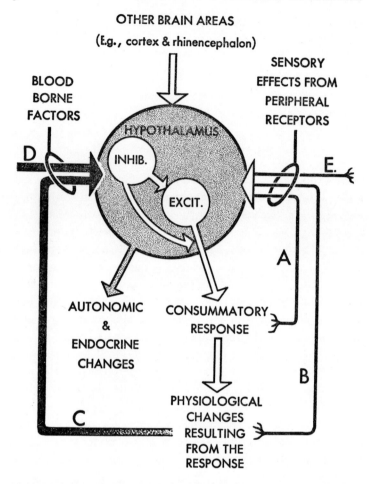

FIGURE 3–2.   Schematic diagram of Stellar's model of the neural and physiological factors that contribute to the control of consummatory behavior assoicated with the primary drives. Description in text. Inhib. = inhibitory center; Excit. = excitatory center. (Modified from Eliot Stellar, "The physiology of motivation." *Psychological Review*, 1954, **61**, 5–22.)

also be the same if the satiation center blocked the output of the excitatory center. Such inhibition would thus terminate the arousal of the drive and also terminate the associated consummatory behavior. As we have already seen, the same type of relation seems to exist between the inspiratory and expiratory centers in the medulla.

Figure 3–2 shows also, as with respiration, that this suggested dual control operates under multiple physiological influences, bloodborne and sensory, both of which can affect the combined activity of the two types of hypothalamic center. For example, the model provides that the consummatory response (chewing, swallowing) has sensory effects (from muscle receptors) that can work backward on the hypothalamus (see A of Figure 3–2). Sensory influences can also arise (see B of Figure 3–2) from such secondary effects associated with the response as the taste of food, moistening of the mouth, or distention of the filled stomach. Further, the model assumes that materials which have been digested and absorbed into the body can also operate directly upon the hypothalamus through the circulating blood (see C of Figure 3–2). All of these feedback influences (see A, B, and C of Figure 3–2) would operate to depress the relevant biological drive. Finally, the model provides that bloodborne factors and sensory influences, independent of the consummatory response itself, can also affect hypothalamic activity (see D and E of Figure 3–2). Such sensory influences would include, for example, the smell of a meal cooking, or the suggested role of stomach contractions in arousing hunger. The production of thirst by the increased concentration of the blood, already discussed, is also an example of a bloodborne effect that clearly is not the result of the consummatory response of drinking. The model also takes account of the fact that the hypothalamus is open to neural influences from elsewhere in the brain. It does not suggest, however, how the appropriate centers in the hypothalamus eventually activate the motor systems that must finally be responsible for the patterned responses that characterize the normal consummatory behavior of the motivated animal. This shortcoming is not unique in the present model, since it is a general mystery how the nervous system manages to develop, store, select, and finally activate patterned chains of responses.

We shall first consider how well the facts about eating and drinking fit Stellar's scheme and consider mating behavior later. For hunger, both an excitatory and an inhibitory center have been approximately located in the hypothalamus. The *satiation center* is located in the vicinity of the ventromedial nucleus. The nucleus itself is commonly referred to as the satiation center, but this is not yet established as a fact. It is entirely possible that only some cells of this nucleus have such a function or, indeed, that the function is managed by other cells nearby or by nerve pathways that pass in the close vicinity. The excitatory *eating center* is located at the same level in the hypothalamus but lies more laterally. Since no particular nucleus approximates this lateral area, the eating center must be characterized anatomically as an ill-defined zone. As with the respiratory centers, both types of hunger center are bilaterally paired, which is the rule for such centers throughout the brain.

The role played by these two centers in the regulation of hunger has been demonstrated experimentally both by damaging them surgically and by stimulating them electrically through buried electrodes permanently fixed in one or the other of them. The first finding to be reported, in the early 1940s, was the dramatic effect of a bilateral surgical lesion in the area of the ventromedial nuclei. The subject animals whose satiation centers had been damaged ate tremendous amounts of food. In the absence of this mechanism for satiation, these *hyperphagic* animals doubled or tripled their weight in a couple of months.

Over the past twenty years, further evidence about these hypothalamic centers has accumulated. As one might expect, ablation of what are now called the eating centers (those in the lateral hypothalamus) produces an animal that starves itself. Such *aphagic* animals are simply not interested in food. Left to their own devices, they eventually starve to death. (Nevertheless, as we shall see, aphagic animals eventually do show substantial recovery if kept alive for a month or so by forced feeding.) The results of electrically stimulating these hypothalamic areas confirm the ablation studies just described. Stimulation of the satiation center reduces eating and stimulation in the lateral hypothalamic zone (the eating center) induces an animal to eat even if it is satiated at the time.

The story of the control of hunger by the hypothalamus sounds neat and trim, but there are still many unanswered problems about the detailed functioning of these centers. For example, investigators would like to know what specific physiological changes are responsible for activating the neurons in these excitatory and inhibitory centers. Considering the apparent functions of the two centers, we might suppose that neurons in the lateral excitatory center are somehow activated by a decrease in the body's food supply; conversely, the satiation center would presumably react to an increase in available food materials. Such a two-way process, however, has not been demonstrated experimentally. This problem is made more difficult since it is not even clear, as already pointed out, what metabolic events elsewhere in the body are critically associated with hunger and satiation.

Some information, nevertheless, is available to suggest how these centers might operate. In the first place, as Figure 3–2 illustrates, investigators have thought that the satiation center suppresses eating by inhibiting the eating center. This type of relationship is supported by the fact that when both the supposed satiation center and the lateral areas are ablated, an experimental animal behaves as though only its lateral hypo-

thalamus had been damaged; the animal refuses to eat. Moreover, electrophysiologists now have shown that electrical activity in the lateral eating center is depressed when, following
a rise in blood sugar, there is increased neural activity in the
satiation center (Anand *et al.,* 1962). The neurons in the
eating center might then have the ability to be spontaneously
active whenever they are not being suppressed by the satiation center. If this were the case, we should expect to find that
there is no specific factor physiologically related to hunger
that has the responsibility of activating the nerve cells in the
eating center. This suggestion does not mean these neurons
would be active without demonstrable cause, but only that
their continuous electrical activity would be the consequence
of the way they are built chemically, or the result of their
connection with some other continuously running system
elsewhere in the brain. It is easier today than it was even a
very few years ago to conceive of circuits in the brain that
function continuously without the necessity of being whipped
into activity by a specific recurrent stimulus.

There is another finding which fits with the idea that the
ventromedial area functions to depress appetite. In anesthetized cats, investigators have recorded increased electrical activity from this area after the injection of amphetamine, a
drug known to depress appetite. Amphetamine still has
some depressant effect on appetite, however, even when the
ventromedial nuclei have been removed surgically. This
serves as another reminder that so-called centers, after all,
are parts of larger circuits, and duplication of function is not
uncommon in the brain.

Added to the basic facts that have now been described,
recent experimental findings have given us new insights into
the role of the lateral hypothalamic area in the regulation of
eating and, for that matter, of drinking. Philip Teitelbaum
and his co-workers, in a methodical and long-term study of

rats made aphagic by lesions in the lateral hypothalamus, discovered that the disorder in these animals involved a deficiency not only in the ingestion of food but also in the ingestion of water (Teitelbaum and Epstein, 1962). Keeping their animals alive by artificial feeding immediately after operation, these workers found that their aphagic rats, over a period of several months, went through a series of recovery stages. As Figure 3–3 shows, these animals are at first both

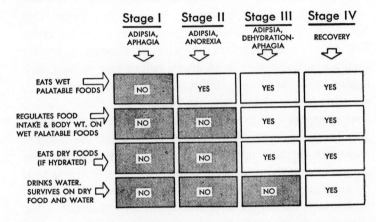

	Stage I ADIPSIA, APHAGIA	Stage II ADIPSIA, ANOREXIA	Stage III ADIPSIA, DEHYDRATION- APHAGIA	Stage IV RECOVERY
EATS WET PALATABLE FOODS	NO	YES	YES	YES
REGULATES FOOD INTAKE & BODY WT. ON WET PALATABLE FOODS	NO	NO	YES	YES
EATS DRY FOODS (IF HYDRATED)	NO	NO	YES	YES
DRINKS WATER. SURVIVES ON DRY FOOD AND WATER	NO	NO	NO	YES

FIGURE 3–3. Table showing the sequence of changes in eating and drinking behavior produced by bilateral lesions in the lateral hypothalamus. Observed behavioral effects are listed at the left; stages of recovery during the postoperative period are indicated at the top. (From Philip Teitelbaum and A. N. Epstein, "The lateral hypothalamic syndrome: recovery of feeding and drinking after lateral hypothalamic lesions." *Psychological Review,* 1962, **69,** 74–90; reprinted with permission of the publisher.)

aphagic and adipsic—they will neither eat nor drink. Several weeks later (Stage II), they still will not drink, but they will eat if the food is both wet and tasty. (Even normal rats will not eat dry food unless there is water to drink.) At this second stage, however, the animals are only, so to speak, taking snacks; they are still unable to regulate their intake of food in a way that is metabolically adequate. In Stage III, the animals start taking biologically appropriate quantities of moist, palatable foodstuffs and will even start eating dry food if they are artificially hydrated by tubing water into their stomachs. In the final stage, a certain number of animals reach full recovery and will properly regulate their intake of both plain water and dry rat food.

It is therefore clear that lateral hypothalamic lesions interfere with the neural mechanisms concerned with both eating and drinking. In fact, it now appears that the aphagia that follows damage to the lateral hypothalamus is caused in the first place by adipsia, and adipsic-aphagic animals recover their ability to regulate food intake before they recover their ability to regulate water intake. It is of interest that, during the early stages of recovery, the brain-damaged animals first start eating as though simply attracted by the taste of palatable foods and only later (Stage III) regulate food intake according to their metabolic need. The investigators have suggested that the recovering animals are first drawn to food by appetite, and only in the later stages of recovery are they driven to it by hunger. Apparently the hypothalamus is involved in the control of both of these kinds of eating behavior; indeed, Stellar's model of the hypothalamus suggests appropriate mechanisms by providing for both sensory and metabolic influences.

These findings indicate that systems of control for eating and drinking overlap in the lateral hypothalamus, but it is nevertheless apparently true that the two systems are separate from each other. Properly placed lesions or stimulation-electrodes can affect an organism's eating but not its drinking, or vice versa. In fact, a recent experiment has shown that the two systems are neurochemically different. Through a tiny tube (micropipette) implanted in the lateral hypothalamus of rats, minute amounts of various chemical compounds that have the ability to stimulate nerve cells were introduced into the rats' brains. Both food and water were available to the animals. When a *cholinergic* compound was injected, the rats started to drink; when an *adrenergic* compound was later inserted down the same micropipette into the same animals, the result was eating instead of drinking (Grossman, 1960). Thus not only are the eating and drinking systems anatomically separate in the lateral hypothalamus, they are neurochemically different as well.

Another investigator, Peter J. Morgane, has suggested in addition that there are two different kinds of system concerned with eating behavior in the lateral hypothalamus (Morgane, 1961). He demonstrated that, aside from the eating center, there is a second hunger zone further lateral in the hypothalamus that appears to have somewhat different functions. Stimulation in this far lateral zone not only makes an animal eat if food is conveniently available, but the stimulated animal is even reported to cross an electrified grid to get food. Such highly motivated behavior is not usually seen when one stimulates the classic eating center in the near lateral hypothalamus. Morgane has suggested further that these drive characteristics of the far lateral zone may be dependent on nerve fibers from the rhinencephalon, farther forward in the brain, that reach the lateral hypothalamus in the medial forebrain bundle (see Figure 2–8). These results fit other findings which show that parts of the rhinencephalon are involved in the control of certain kinds of motivated behavior (see Chapter 5).

Many details of the control of water intake were mentioned in connection with the regulation of food intake, but there are other facts about the control of drinking behavior still to be described. For one thing, a specific inhibitory center for drinking so far has not been found. On the other hand, since it has been discovered that the systems for eating and drink-

ing overlap so intimately in the excitatory region of the lateral
hypothalamus, it might be worthwhile to analyze more carefully the ingestion patterns of animals that have been made
hyperphagic by lesions in the ventromedial hypothalamus. It
might turn out that an inhibitory drinking mechanism is similarly located in close connection with the ventromedial satiation center for eating, but this remains to be determined experimentally.

Excitatory areas specifically related to drinking, however,
have been demonstrated in the hypothalamus. For example, it
is possible to make a completely water-satiated goat drink as
much as seven liters of water by stimulating its anterior hypothalamus electrically and this result has been demonstrated in
other species as well. Experimenters do not know how this
area in the anterior hypothalamus is related to the excitatory
thirst system located more posteriorly in the lateral hypothalamus. The same effect on drinking can be obtained if, instead
of electrical stimulation, a minute drop of concentrated salt
solution is applied to the same anterior hypothalamic area
through an implanted micropipette. This second finding is of
particular interest because physiological experiments suggest,
as we have already seen, that the dehydration of certain brain
cells might be the manner in which the body's need for water
is signaled to the central nervous system, and concentrated
salt solution is known to dehydrate cells with which it comes
into contact. Caution is needed in making such an interpreta-
tion, however, since it is known that salt solution has the general ability to stimulate nerve cells, probably through its capacity to produce changes in intracellular water and mineral
balance. Thus it cannot yet be said that the effect of salt in
the hypothalamus is really specific for the drinking behavior it
induces, although that is a reasonable possibility. If the thirst
system in the hypothalamus eventually proves to have a specific sensitivity to concentrated solutions, such an effect pre-

sumably would operate through osmoreceptors that, for other reasons, are suspected of being in the hypothalamus. Such central receptors would sense changes in the osmotic pressure (concentration) of the circulating blood.

Not only can the hypothalamus help regulate the water balance of the body through its influence on drinking behavior, it also has control over a related hormonal adjustment. Through its connections with the pituitary gland, hypothalamic activity, as already mentioned, can lead to the secretion of the antidiuretic hormone (ADH). This hormone produces changes in the kidney that result in the retention of body water. Such a defensive maneuver is important to a dehydrated and thirsty animal. Reasonably enough, increased secretion of ADH has been reported following electrical stimulation in the anterior hypothalamus which simultaneously produced increased drinking. This combined mechanism of regulation is a good example of the fact that the hypothalamus can influence both the consummatory behavior and the autonomic and endocrine adjustments related to the biological drives. Other examples of the same kind will come up when we turn to the consideration of sexual drive and mating behavior.

There is a study of water ingestion which experimentally demonstrates the fact that the performance of a consummatory response can in itself influence the course of further ingestion (see A of Figure 3–2). In this study, dogs were prepared by putting a small hole in the esophagus and sewing the edges of this opening to a small slit made in the skin of the neck. Everything swallowed by the animal then drains through this external opening (*fistula*) and does not reach the stomach. (The animals can be given the food and water they need by a tube inserted through the fistula into the stomach.) The interesting result is that these fistulated animals, when thirsty, drink an appropriate quantity of water and then stop

—even though none of the ingested water actually goes into the stomach. This finding apparently means that the act of swallowing can in itself send sensory (proprioceptive) information to the brain, possibly to the hypothalamus, by which the amount of drinking can be monitored and appropriately terminated. So far, however, this proposed feedback mechanism has only been inferred from observations of the behavior of fistulated animals. Neural activity in the hypothalamus, correlated with swallowing, has not yet been demonstrated experimentally.

Hypothalamic Regulation
of Mating Behavior

Mating behavior is concerned with the perpetuation of the species rather than with the survival of the individual, and is supported accordingly by an elaborate hormonal mechanism related to the reproductive functions. Moreover, the final consummatory response in sexual behavior is copulation, as contrasted with ingestion. For these reasons hypothalamic regulation of mating behavior may be considered separately, although many of the general considerations about how the hypothalamus contributes to the regulation of eating and drinking apply equally to mating behavior. In many respects, the model shown in Figure 3–2 is applicable although, as with hunger and thirst, direct proof is not at present available for all the channels of influence suggested by the model. On the other hand, the extensive studies of sexual behavior by the comparative psychologist Frank A. Beach and the experimental anatomist William C. Young, as well as investigations by many other workers, make it amply clear that normal mating behavior is indeed dependent on the type of sensory and hormonal influences suggested by Stellar's hypothalamic model (e.g., see Beach, 1947; Young, 1961).

The anatomical, physiological, and behavioral support of reproductive activities is crucially dependent on the presence of the proper sex hormones. For instance, the development and maintenance of the primary and secondary sexual structures in the female requires proper amounts of several different hormones. Proper timing and balance among several different hormones are also necessary to govern the reproductive cycle that culminates in the periodic release of eggs (*ovulation*), and, when the eggs have been fertilized, shifts in these hormonal mechanisms are necessary to support the physiological processes which permit the normal development of the embryo. In the male, more simply, only a single sex hormone is involved in maintaining the development and function of the genital structures and the secondary sexual characteristics of the body in general.

The female's sexual behavior depends in largest part on one sexual hormone, *estrogen*. While it has other reproductive functions, this is the female hormone that appears to have the largest role in the nervous system's control of mating. Recent studies, however, suggest that a second female hormone, *progesterone,* is more important for optimal mating than once was thought the case. Investigators have known for some time that maximal sexual receptivity in the female rat and guinea pig requires both estrogen and progesterone, and it now seems this may be true for certain higher species as well. The single masculine sex hormone, *testosterone,* is the male counterpart of estrogen, and it alone supplies the hormonal basis of male sexual behavior. Both estrogen and testosterone are produced by the sex glands or *gonads:* the ovaries in the female and testes in the male.

Like the other biological drives, mating behavior is influenced to some degree by activity at a number of levels in the central nervous system, even though the hypothalamus seems to be a major integrating center and the highest essential center in the brainstem. The neocortex supplies an excitatory sexual influence, and, in some of the higher species, apparently also contributes to the effective motor performance of the normal sequence of copulatory responses. The contribution of the cortex to mating behavior is strikingly greater in the male than in the female for all of the species that have been studied. In addition, certain structures in the rhinencephalon have an inhibitory influence on the copulatory behavior of the male; bilateral lesions near the amygdala produce remarkable hypersexuality in male cats and monkeys as well as in man. Scientists believe that such brain damage in the rhinencephalon releases hypothalamic mechanisms from some type of inhibitory influence normally imposed by these higher structures. As with cortical lesions, damage to the rhinencephalon apparently has little or no effect on the pattern of mating behavior in the female, at least in the species so far studied—cats, rabbits, and rats. Female mating behavior seems more exclusively dependent on the lower hypothalamic level of integration.

Now let us return to the hypothalamus, the brain structure which has received the most intensive study in connection with mating behavior. There is clear evidence that it contains excitatory centers for mating behavior in both sexes. As with the comparable centers for hunger and thirst, experimental damage leads to deficiency or total loss of mating behavior. So far, the existence of these centers has been demonstrated only in infraprimate mammals such as rats and cats, but there is no reason to suppose that they are not the same in principle in monkeys and in man.

In both male and female, the hypothalamic excitatory centers for mating behavior are of two distinct types. One type, the *gonadotrophic center,* initiates the secretion of the gonadotrophic hormones by the pituitary which, in turn, regulate the secretion of the respective sex hormones by the gonads. When a lesion is made in this hormonal excitatory center in the hypothalamus, the secretion of estrogen in the female or testosterone in the male is no longer adequate to support reproductive activity—including mating behavior. The center is thus excitatory for mating behavior only in an indirect way; it is not itself a behavior center. Investigators have shown that the loss of mating behavior that follows damage to the gonadotrophic centers can be reversed by treatment with the appropriate sex hormone. These studies have made it clear that such surgical lesions do not interfere directly with the neural circuits involved in the performance of copulation itself.

On the other hand, the second type of sexual excitatory center in the hypothalamus is apparently concerned directly with behavior. Sufficient damage to this so-called *sex-behavior center* results in a loss of mating behavior which no amount of treatment with sex hormones can correct. As we should expect, there is at the same time no evidence of pituitary or gonadal abnormality in this latter type of brain-damaged animal.

In the cat, guinea pig, and rat, the sex-behavior center of the hypothalamus has been found to be located more anteriorly than the gonadotrophic center, which in turn occupies a position near or slightly behind the base of the stalk of the pituitary gland. In the rabbit, however, the behavioral center is posterior to the hormonal center, which is nevertheless found in its usual position near the stalk of the pituitary. Some investigators have suggested that there may be still a second behavioral center in the more usual position, in the anterior hypothalamus of the rabbit, though this fact has not as yet been successfully demonstrated.

Because sex hormones are necessary for the initiation and

performance of mating behavior, the function of the sex-behavior center in the hypothalamus is thought to be dependent in some way on the presence of the appropriate hormone (see D of Figure 3–2). For example, estrogen or testosterone might increase neural activity in the sex-behavior center or influence the timing of its neural circuits. That the sex hormones have such effects has not yet been directly demonstrated by electrophysiologists. It is now known, however, that sexual behavior can be initiated in a rat by introducing a minute amount of estrogen or testosterone directly into the hypothalamus.

An interesting sidelight on this problem is the recent research in embryology, which has demonstrated that the sex hormones also play a role in the prenatal development of sex-specific mating behavior. These workers gave large injections of testosterone to pregnant guinea pigs during certain periods of their pregnancy and found that female offspring were born with masculinized genitals and, furthermore, showed distinctly male characteristics in their sexual behavior after they had matured (Young *et al.*, 1964). These results suggest that during embryonic development hormones influence the organization of the neural circuits that mediate mating behavior. Presumably the female hormone of both mother and female embryo supports the development of female behavioral potentialities in the female offspring, while a male offspring offsets the influence of the female hormone with his own production of male hormone. At present, it is only conjectural that the prenatal influence of sex hormones on later mating behavior involves the shaping of hypothalamic neural circuits, although this is a reasonable guess.

While two types of excitatory center for mating behavior have thus been identified in the hypothalamus, there is no firm agreement as to the existence of a hypothalamic inhibitory center for mating behavior. Various small hypothalamic lesions, both anterior and posterior of the gonadotropic center, have been reported to lead to hypersexuality in some cases, suggesting that an inhibitory system had been disrupted. Investigators, however, have still not systematically localized the neural basis of these effects. There is some recent evidence to suggest that a sexual satiation center may be located in the border zone between the hypothalamus and the midbrain just behind it. There is clearly an inhibitory influence on masculine mating behavior, already mentioned, that originates in the rhinencephalon; furthermore, there are a number of important pathways that interconnect the rhinencephalon and the hypothalamus (see Figure 2–8).

From what is known about eating and drinking, one can only infer the existence of the influence of feedback on the hypothalamus arising from the performance of the consummatory response (see A of Figure 3–2). In mating behavior, however, such sensory feedback has now been directly demonstrated by recording electrically from the anterior hypothalamus during artificial vaginal stimulation in both the cat and the rabbit.

4

THE RETICULAR FORMATION: AROUSAL SYSTEM FOR THE FOREBRAIN

WITHIN the reticular formation in the core of the brainstem, many incoming sensory fibers converge and a great variety of motor fibers originate. For the simpler vertebrate animals, in which the diencephalon and telencephalon are as yet poorly developed, this complex zone in the brainstem appears to be one of the areas in the brain most suitably arranged to integrate incoming and outgoing neural information. In the more complex mammals, however, with a greatly enlarged forebrain and its expanded neocortex, the reticular formation was originally considered only a reflex center, solely concerned with such basic activities as the control of respiration and the function of the heart. In contrast to these physiological reflexes, psychological events such as learning, perception, and attention were thought to be mediated chiefly by the neocortex and the rapidly conducting afferent and efferent pathways connecting it with the periphery. In this older division of function, scientists viewed the reticular formation largely as a motor center, ignoring its ascending pathways in spite of their being so well known anatomically.

Only within the last fifteen years have the ascending or *sensory* functions of the reticular formation come to be better understood, particularly in their relation to the function of the neocortex. The anatomy of this ascending reticular system (ARS) is discussed in some detail in Chapter 2. Its ascending influences are shown diagrammatically, in summary form, in Figure 4–1. Briefly, the reticular formation, as it

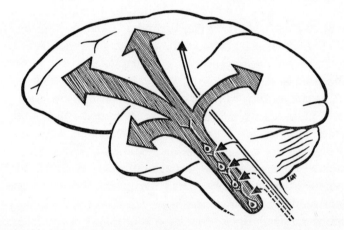

FIGURE 4–1. Summary diagram illustrating some of the afferent and efferent pathways of the ascending reticular system (ARS) superimposed on the brain of a monkey. The ARS (shaded area) is composed of short neuron chains up through the core of the brainstem to the thalamus and longer, thalamo-cortical projection fibers that fan out diffusely over the neocortex. The solid black lines in the dorsal brainstem represent specific sensory pathways, on their way to the cortex, that send collateral branches into the ARS. As shown by the dashed arrows, some fibers in the specific sensory systems feed their sensory input exclusively into the brainstem reticular formation. (Modified from D. B. Lindsley, "Attention, consciousness, sleep and wakefulness." In John Field, H. W. Magoun, and V. E. Hall, eds., *Handbook of Physiology, Section I: Neurophysiology*, Vol. III. Washington, D.C.: American Physiological Society, 1960. Pp. 1553–1593.)

forms a polysynaptic pathway through the core of the brain-stem, receives both direct projection fibers and collateral nerve fibers from the specific sensory systems and, in turn, makes synaptic connections with cells in the diencephalon which project diffusely on the cerebral cortex. In addition to this sensory input from peripheral receptors, the ARS also receives a large afferent input from the cortex itself, as well as from other forebrain structures (see Figure 2–7). These separate but overlapping afferent contributions to the reticular formation provide a dual mechanism that can modify ARS activity; that is to say, the activity of the reticular formation can be altered by sensory input from the periphery and by input coming down from the forebrain. In this way, reciprocal connections exist between the reticular formation and the cortex so that each is capable of having its electrical activity influenced by the other.

Current concern with the cortical influence of the ARS is based partly on the interest of scientists in understanding the neural mechanisms responsible for maintaining consciousness. A state of consciousness or awareness is assumed to be essential for most adaptive behavioral events to occur. Such awareness is presumably shared by at least all vertebrates. Considerable problems arise, however, when one tries to define operationally such terms as *consciousness* or *awareness*. Because of these problems, *wakefulness* has been used as a term roughly synonymous with consciousness, and, as we shall see, present-day interest in the ARS stems from the experimental demonstration that ARS activity is essential to maintaining the waking state.

Reticular Control of
the EEG and Wakefulness

An operational definition of wakefulness or sleep has been derived from correlating the behavioral activity of a subject, animal or human, with the general electrical activity emanating from the surface of the brain. A recording of this electrical activity can be obtained directly from the surface of the brain itself, an *electrocorticogram* or *ECG,* or it can be recorded indirectly from the scalp, an *electroencephalogram* or *EEG.* The EEG, which is more commonly used, provides a continuous record of the fluctuations in voltage which are constantly occurring at the surface of the brain, even though the electrical changes are recorded from the scalp. These electrical fluctuations are very small and the major function of the EEG machine is to amplify them and provide a continuous record of their changes.

To obtain an EEG, a series of electrodes, metal discs with a good conducting surface, are applied to the scalp. These electrodes are connected to an amplifier and the voltage fluctuations obtained are recorded by an ink-writer on a moving strip of paper, with one pen for each electrode. An example of the resulting record is shown in Figure 4–2. The left-hand part of the record shows one of the characteristic EEG patterns of a sleeping cat. As can be seen, the changes in electrical activity during sleep are relatively large (high voltage) and occur relatively infrequently. This sleeping record is thus characterized by high voltage, slow activity (HVS). An EEG that shows high voltage, slow activity is one of the commonest types of tracing recorded during sleep, although the details of the EEG pattern vary with different stages of sleep. As also can be seen from the record shown in Figure 4–2, the charac-

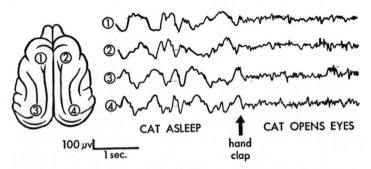

CAT ASLEEP   ↑   CAT OPENS EYES

100 µv|_____   hand
            1 sec.   clap

FIGURE 4–2. Diagram showing the shift in the EEG pattern as a sleeping cat is awakened by a sudden noise. The numbers superimposed on the top view of a cat brain at the left indicate the brain areas from which the four EEG tracings to the right were recorded. For further description, see text. (Modified from D. B. Lindsley, L. H. Schreiner, W. B. Knowles, and H. W. Magoun, "Behavioral and EEG changes following chronic brainstem lesions in the cat." *Electroencephalography and Clinical Neurophysiology,* 1950, **2**, 483–498.)

ter of the EEG changes markedly when the sleeping cat is aroused by a sudden noise. The high voltage slow waves are replaced by very small waves (low voltage) of higher frequency, so-called low voltage, fast activity (LVF). This latter pattern is characteristic of the waking state and the animal shows behavioral signs that are consistent with this; the eyes are opened, the head raised, and eventually the animal moves about.

HVS activity is sometimes referred to as a *synchronized* EEG pattern, while the LVF activity is often described as a *desynchronized* or *activation* pattern. The relationship between the EEG pattern and the sleep–wakefulness cycle is found not only in cats but in all mammals, including man. We can conclude, therefore, that a subject is awake if his EEG shows LVF activity and that he is asleep if it shows some form of HVS activity. This correlation has had important use in many experimental studies of the ARS.

Over ten years before the ascending influences of the ARS were recognized, Frederic Bremer, a Belgian neurophysiologist, demonstrated that the brainstem was necessary for the maintenance of the cyclic pattern of the EEG that normally accompanies the alternating periods of wakefulness and sleep. Working with cats, Bremer showed that, when an animal's central nervous system is completely transected at the bottom of the brainstem where it joins the spinal cord (an *encephale isolé* preparation), the paralyzed animal's EEG continues to show normal cycles of sleep and waking activity. If, however, the nervous system is cut through at the top of the brainstem in the midbrain (a *cerveau isolé* preparation), the EEG shows continuous HVS activity indicative of sleep, and the operated animal cannot be aroused for any length of time greater than a few seconds (see Figure 4–3).

Bremer, along with other investigators who have subsequently worked on this problem, demonstrated further that visual and olfactory input, entering the brain above the midbrain transection of the *cerveau isolé* preparation, do not provide sufficient sensory support to maintain even intermittent wakefulness. The sensory input from the muscles and skin of the face, however, entering the brain through the fifth cranial nerve (trigeminal nerve), is critical for maintaining such arousal. A transection of the brain can be made at any level in the brainstem below the entrance of this fifth nerve in the pons and the animal will still maintain the normal EEG pattern which is correlated with cyclical waking and sleeping. If the brain is transected above the entrance of this sensory nerve, however, the EEG shows permanent HVS activity and the animal remains somnolent. Furthermore, if the brainstem transection is made below the entrance of the fifth nerve and that nerve itself is subsequently cut, the EEG activity becomes identical to that seen after a higher transection, such as in the *cerveau isolé* preparation.

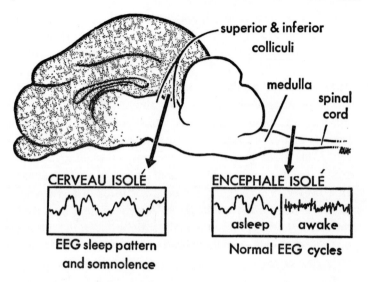

FIGURE 4–3.   Diagram of a medial view of the cat brain showing the immediate effect of sectioning the brainstem at two different levels on the EEG pattern and the sleep–wakefulness cycle. The arrows represent the two levels of transection. The high and low levels of transection, respectively, produce animal preparations that Bremer labeled the *cerveau isolé* and the *encephale isolé*.

There is no doubt about the immediate loss of wakefulness in the *cerveau isolé* preparation. Some workers, however, have claimed that such an operated animal, if kept alive for two weeks or so, eventually will show an occasional LVF pattern in its EEG, suggesting that the neocortex has regained the ability to be "awake." Apparently, some brain center above the midbrain transection, possibly in the diencephalon, can take over the job of arousing the cortex.

These experiments, while demonstrating the importance of sensory input to the brainstem for wakefulness, do not demonstrate how these sensory nerve impulses help maintain the necessary electrical arousal in the forebrain.

The crucial experiments that established the role of the reticular formation itself in the maintenance of EEG arousal were performed by Horace W. Magoun and his collaborators throughout the late 1940s and early 1950s (Magoun, 1963). It all started in 1949, when the Italian neurophysiologist Giuseppe Moruzzi and Magoun first showed that stimulation of the midbrain reticular formation in the sleeping cat produced both behavioral and EEG evidence of wakefulness or arousal (Moruzzi and Magoun, 1949). Indeed, the EEG records in their study were the same whether electrical stimulation in the midbrain was used or whether the animal was awakened with a natural stimulus such as a sudden noise. In both cases, the changes in the EEG pattern were like those shown in the record in Figure 4–2.

Subsequently, other workers have shown in a number of ways that this effect cannot be attributed to stimulation of the specific sensory systems that travel through the brainstem but rather is due to the direct stimulation of the reticular formation itself. For example, when an animal is anesthetized with a sedative like one of the barbiturates, the specific sensory pathways (as for touch or hearing) continue to conduct nerve impulses to the cortex without any impairment; in such an anesthetized animal, however, the reticular formation is unable to conduct nerve impulses at all and is electrically silent. Similarly, during the coma which commonly follows a severe head injury, the reticular formation is also electrically silent while the specific sensory pathways appear to conduct impulses in a relatively normal manner.

More recent experiments have fractionated anatomically the lesion in Bremer's *cerveau isolé* preparation to determine its essential component; these studies also support the idea that the ARS is the system in the brainstem that is essential for the state of wakefulness. Restricted transection of the specific sensory pathways in the brainstem does not affect the normal sleeping and waking patterns of the EEG. On the other hand, if the lesion in the brainstem selectively cuts through the reticular formation and thus eliminates its ascending influences while sparing the specific sensory pathways, the EEG shows constant HVS activity and the animal cannot be aroused (Lindsley, 1960). These effects of different lesions in the brainstem are presented graphically in Figure 4–4.

Neural activity within the reticular formation itself is not directly responsible for the maintenance of wakefulness; it only performs this function through its secondary influences

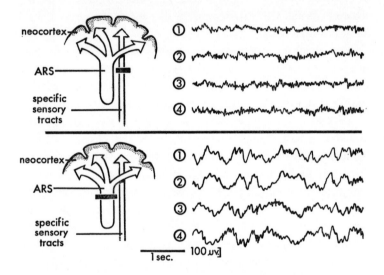

FIGURE 4–4.   Diagram comparing the effect of two different brainstem lesions on the EEG pattern of the cat. The top diagram shows the effect of sectioning (heavy bar) the specific sensory pathways; the EEG tracings to the right show that a waking pattern (LVF) can still be obtained. The diagram below shows that section of the ascending reticular system (ARS) results in a permanent sleep pattern in the EEG (HVS). See text for further description. Numbers have the same meaning as in Figure 4–2. (Based on material from D. B. Lindsley, L. H. Schreiner, W. B. Knowles, and H. W. Magoun, "Behavioral and EEG changes following chronic brainstem lesions in the cat." *Electroencephalography and Clinical Neurophysiology*, 1950, **2**, 483–498.)

on other parts of the brain, particularly on the neocortex. In man, at least, the cortex also is thought necessary for the maintenance of wakefulness. For example, the degeneration of the cortex and related subcortical pathways which follows brain damage has been reported as producing persistent coma such as that seen with brainstem lesions in experimental animals. Cortex and reticular formation thus are thought to act together as the major neural systems participating in the cyclical activity of sleeping and wakefulness.

In this interacting system, the reticular formation appears to exert two separate types of effect on the cortex. The maintenance of a state of wakefulness for a prolonged period, such as all day, is an example of a continuous, or *tonic,* effect of reticular formation influence upon the cortex. A transitory, or *phasic,* effect is exemplified by the sudden change in the level of arousal when an individual shifts from sleep to wakefulness or when he is briefly stirred from a drowsy state to one of alertness. Neurophysiologists believe that tonic arousal depends primarily on the portion of the ARS in the brainstem, while the phasic changes in alertness are handled by the portion of the reticular system in the thalamus.

The characteristics of the ARS conform to much of what was already known about sleep before the contribution of the reticular system was recognized. For example, any person preparing for sleep knows well the importance of cutting down sensory stimulation; all types of stimulation, from the external environment as well as from within the body, are capable of raising the level of neural activity in the ARS. Excessive mental activity can also hold sleep in abeyance; the recurrent pathways by which the forebrain can activate the ARS may be the route over which such self-arousal can operate.

More formally, many of the details of Nathaniel Kleitman's so-called evolutionary theory of sleep, first proposed in the 1930s, are understandable in terms of the function and connections of the ARS. Kleitman, the University of Chicago physiologist who pioneered the scientific study of sleep, pointed out that the primitive sleep–wakefulness cycle, as seen in simpler animals and young persons, involves only what he called the *wakefulness of necessity*. The organism is aroused reflexly from sleep by the pressure of periodic sensory events arising in the external environment or, more particularly, in the internal environment of the body. When the stimulation subsides, the organism falls to sleep again; in this way Kleitman explained the primitive *polyphasic* sleep–wakefulness cycle.

In the adult forms of more complex animals and quite conspicuously in the adult person, a *monophasic* cycle develops in which most typically there are single long periods of sleep and wakefulness that approximately match the diurnal light–dark cycle. The wakefulness seen in this more advanced case was characterized by Kleitman as the *wakefulness of choice*. He proposed that such day-long wakefulness is a learned ability and suggested, accordingly, that there must be some neural apparatus by which higher brain centers can come to influence the "wakefulness center," which he postulated as located somewhere in the brainstem. The ARS and its multiplicity of inputs and outputs seemingly could supply the neuroanatomical system Kleitman envisioned.

In recent years, many more details of the sleep process have been discovered (Kleitman, 1963); psychologists and physiologists are even starting to learn something about the neural mechanisms of dreaming. The ARS and the EEG patterns that parallel changes in the activity of the ARS are the neural system and the neurophysiological indicator that are most commonly involved in modern research on this topic.

Thalamic Level of the ARS

Thus far we have been considering the importance of the reticular formation in the production and maintenance of the wakeful state, particularly as this is reflected in alterations in the electrical activity of the cortex. The route which the pathways of the ARS take through the diencephalon, particularly through the thalamus, as well as the mechanism through which cortical arousal is obtained remain to be considered.

As we have already seen in Chapter 2, the reticular formation in the brainstem projects dorsally both to the midline and intralaminar nuclei of the thalamus as well as to the subthalamus. It also projects ventrally to the hypothalamus (see Figure 2–7). Each of these areas would be anatomically appropriate for relaying the ascending reticular influences forward to brain structures in the telencephalon. The ventral pathway travels through the hypothalamus and enters the septum and hippocampus of the limbic system. Since the hippocampus is known to project on the cortex and both hippocampus and cortex undergo characteristic changes in electrical activity with sleep and wakefulness, this ventral route could be one pathway over which cortical arousal is mediated by the ARS. If such is the case, it is clearly not the only available route for this purpose, for bilateral removal of the hippocampus does not interfere with the normal arousal of the cortex.

The dorsal pathway of the ARS, through the thalamus, is thought more likely to be the essential one for cortical arousal, and, with this possibility in mind, neurophysiologist Herbert H. Jasper and his collaborators at McGill University in Montreal have particularly studied the function of the diffuse pathways that project from the thalamus to the cortex (Jasper, 1960). Even within these thalamo-cortical pathways, however, there are several alternative routes possible, and it is not yet sure which are the more important.

Research has focused primarily on two areas within the thalamus, the midline-intralaminar nuclei and the so-called reticular nucleus. The reticular nucleus has seemed likely to be involved in cortical arousal since it is the only known area of the thalamus in which fibers arise that project diffusely over the surface of the cortex. Physiological studies have implicated the midline-intralaminar nuclei in the arousal system because electrical stimulation at this site has an effect similar to stimulating the ARS down in the brainstem—the EEG of a sleeping animal shifts, at least for a short time, to the waking pattern and the animal rouses from sleep.

As has already been noted, the arousal that results from stimulating the thalamic portions of the reticular system is typically shorter-lived than that which results from brainstem stimulation; arousal initiated from the thalamus may only last for a few seconds while arousal following brainstem stimulation can persist for some minutes after the stimulating current has ceased. The transient nature of thalamic arousal led Jasper to suggest that the thalamic part of the reticular system may normally be responsible for initiating momentary surges in the psychological arousal or attention of awake organisms that necessarily must shift from second to second, in keeping with changing environmental demands. In line with this suggestion it is interesting to note that stimulation of the thalamic reticular system can lead to the separate arousal of more discrete portions of the cortex than is commonly seen following stimulation of the root of the ARS in the brainstem.

Paradoxically, certain frequencies of stimulation in the thalamic portion of the ARS can disrupt the arousal system and induce sleep. Some investigators have suggested that this disruption of the arousal system results from a frequency of thalamic stimulation that favors the activity of certain thalamic neurons that are known to be capable of inhibiting output from elsewhere in the thalamus.

The electrophysiological mechanism by which arousal is induced in the individual cortical neurons is as yet little understood. One type of EEG response, the *cortical recruitment response,* has been studied extensively and may supply some answers to this question since it is analogous in some ways to the arousal response of the EEG. The cortical recruitment response is produced by electrical stimulation of the midline-intralaminar nuclei in the thalamus at frequencies of 6 to 12 per second. It is characterized by the gradual growth of a widespread negative electric charge over the surface of the cortex. It is called a recruitment response because it increases in a stepwise manner as though more and more neurons were being recruited in the cortical process initiated by the thalamic stimulation.

Neurophysiologists think that the recruitment response of the cortex may shed some light on the mechanism of arousal, since it is initiated from the reticular system and results in measurable changes in the excitability of nerve cells in the layers of the cortex. Certain cortical cells become easier to stimulate when a recruitment response is occurring, and, when the response reaches its peak, some neurons that were previously not firing at all begin to send out nerve impulses in rhythm with the thalamic stimulation. The recruitment response seemingly represents an induced electrical change in the dendrites of certain cortical neurons; these, in turn, increase the excitability of the cells.

The recruiting response is not identical with the arousal mechanism, however, because it is not abolished when an animal is totally anesthetized with a barbiturate. Moreover, damage to the anterior thalamus, which blocks the cortical recruitment response, has no effect on an animal's general state of arousal. While the cortical recruitment response may well be instructive as to the cellular mechanisms underlying cortical arousal, seemingly it cannot itself be the sole electrophysiological change that accounts for this arousal.

Reticular Influences on Sensory Systems

Wakefulness is obviously a necessary precursor for most other behavioral activities and is the foundation on which such psychological processes as perception, learning, and thinking must be built. In this sense, the reticular formation is obviously involved in these complex psychological activities. A few recent experiments, however, have suggested that the ARS may be to some extent directly involved in more complex behavioral functions.

Research workers have shown, for example, that the reticular formation plays a direct role in determining which sensory signals are allowed to enter the central nervous system. This type of function seemingly conforms to the more general characteristics of the ARS that we have already considered. That is, an animal, aroused by some event of the moment, clearly would profit by attending selectively to the more important sensory signals entering the brain and by blocking the intrusion of other, less urgent ones. Electrophysiologists have now demonstrated that selective attention does involve such a process.

Investigators working with cats implanted recording electrodes in the nuclei through which auditory signals must pass as they enter the brain. Electrical responses then can be recorded from these auditory nuclei in the brainstem each time a sound, such as a click, is presented in the immediate environment, and these workers studied the manner in which this electrical response changed under various conditions.

They found that the size of this electrical auditory signal, and thus how much it intrudes on other brain activity, depends on how much the cat is attending to the clicking sound. For example, if the click is presented continuously, in a monotonous rhythm, the electrical response occurring to each click soon diminishes in size—the cat has adapted to this meaningless repetitive stimulus and ceases to pay much attention to it.

A similar shift in auditory attention, along with the resulting diminution of the electrical response, takes place quite abruptly if another more attractive stimulus, such as a mouse, is presented simultaneously to the cat. The cat promptly stops listening to the click in order to watch the mouse, and the auditory signal in the brain accordingly shrinks in size. The auditory response then can be returned to its original size by pairing the click with an electric shock to the cat's foot; the click has become important again and so commands the animal's attention.

Neural pathways that are able in this way to modulate sensory signals as they enter the brain are called *centrifugal* pathways and are thought to exist for all the senses. It was once believed that these centrifugal pathways originated only within the reticular formation. It is now known, however, that similar effects can be produced by stimulating particular points in the cortex. Some have suggested that the centrifugal suppression of sensory input to the nervous system might be the mechanism that underlies the various psychiatric anesthesias such as blindness, deafness, and numbness which are commonly seen in hysterical patients. Whether this proves to be so, the selective filtering of information as it enters the brain over the sensory pathways seems relevant to the processes of arousal and attention, which appear to be some of the main concerns of the ARS.

Not only does the ARS help determine the intensity with which sensory signals enter the brain; it also can influence the pattern of sensory processes within the central nervous system. Experiments have shown, for example, that two flashes of light, when presented in very rapid succession, are recorded as only one electrical response in the lateral geniculate nucleus (the specific thalamic nucleus for vision). Since the lateral geniculate nucleus is the structure that relays visual information to the cortex, the same blurring of the discrete visual signals occurs at the cortical level as well. When this happens, electrophysiologists know that the animal is unable to detect the two flashes of light as separate stimuli; the lights have fused and only one flash is apparent. If the reticular formation is stimulated simultaneously with the presentation of the same two rapid flashes of light, however, they can be recorded separately in the lateral geniculate and the cortex as two different sensory events. This experiment suggests that changes in the environment may become more easily detected by an aroused and attending animal as the result of the related increase of activity in the ARS.

One behavioral scientist has studied directly how the detectability and discriminability of rapidly presented objects are influenced by stimulation of the ARS (Fuster, 1958). Monkeys were used in this study. They were required to select the correct one of two objects, the one under which a food-reward was always available. The length of time that the stimulus-objects were exposed could be varied and the apparatus was so arranged that the time from the presentation of the stimuli to the time the monkey made the selection was automatically recorded (reaction time). At certain periods during this test, the midbrain reticular formation was stimulated with electrodes that were permanently implanted in the brains of the experimental monkeys. This reticular stimulation produced an improved performance. There were fewer errors and a decreased reaction time. Stimulation of the reticular formation seemingly enhanced the monkey's ability to discriminate between rapidly presented stimuli.

The interdependence of the subcortical ARS and the neo-cortex in the maintenance of normal behavior is worth final emphasis. Without the cortex, mammalian subcortical centers such as the reticular formation cannot be counted on to elaborate patterns of behavior that are sufficiently adaptive to ensure survival of the animal. Without the reticular formation, on the other hand, the cortex is not able to maintain even such a primitive function as wakefulness.

5

SUBCORTICAL
MECHANISMS OF
REWARD AND
PUNISHMENT

REWARD AND PUNISHMENT are words used in everyday language. If we like what a person is doing and wish it to be repeated, we give a reward. On the other hand, we punish a person's behavior when we do not approve of it and would like to have it stopped. In place of these everyday terms, the behavioral scientist uses two roughly synonymous expressions; he refers to a reward as a *positive reinforcement* and a punishment as a *negative reinforcement*. These terms can be defined in the following way. An event serves as a positive reinforcement if it increases the frequency or promptness of the pattern of behavior with which it is associated. Conversely, a negative reinforcement either decreases the frequency of any behavior which it consistently follows or increases the frequency or promptness of behavior that leads to the termination of the punishing reinforcement. Food or water, for example, is a positive reinforcer for a hungry or thirsty animal. A negative reinforcement is usually a painful stimulus; an electric shock is the commonest negative reinforcement used in behavioral experiments.

Basic reinforcing agents such as food, water, and the pain associated with electric shock are usually called *primary* reinforcements to distinguish them from more subtle reinforcers such as, for example, a token that can be used to obtain food, a look out of a window for an animal that has been restrained in a visually uninteresting environment or, at the human level, a harsh word of reprimand. All reinforcing agents are thus materials or events that can induce organisms to change their pattern of behavior; animals will adaptively alter their performance to obtain positive reinforcement or avoid negative. Most psychologists feel that the largest share of learned behavior is developed on the basis of such reinforcement.

Mostly because of the apparent importance of reinforcement in the learning process, investigators have been interested in gaining a better understanding of how the process of reinforcement works. As the result of numerous experimental studies over the years, psychologists have learned many of the rules that determine how various types and patterns of reinforcement will influence behavior. Moreover, physiological workers have discovered many of the mechanisms by which the body controls the consummatory responses associated with primary positive reinforcers like food and water (see Chapter 3). Only recently, however, have scientists started to study directly the brain systems that underlie the process of reinforcement.

Brain Stimulation as a Reinforcement

Largely through the use of a single ingenious experimental method, research workers over the last ten years have begun to learn something about these reinforcement mechanisms in the brain. These investigators implant an electrode in various parts of an animal's brain and use electrical stimulation through this electrode as a reinforcement. They time the electrical stimulus so that it occurs in conjunction with some behavior of the animal that the experimenter wishes to influence. Intracranial stimulation thus is used as if it were an external reinforcing event like some rewarding food or a punishing electric shock. The reinforcing properties of brain stimulation were demonstrated almost simultaneously in 1954 by James Olds and Peter Milner at McGill University and by Jose Delgado and his associates, Warren Roberts and Neal Miller, at Yale University. Their pioneering experiments demonstrated that intracranial stimulation could be used to study the anatomical localization as well as the general characteristics of reinforcement systems in the brain.

Olds and Milner (1954) studied rats placed in a modified version of the commonly used Skinner box in which experimental animals learn to obtain a reward (typically food or water) by depressing a lever inside the box. In their experiments, however, the apparatus was arranged so that each time the rat pressed the lever in the box, a small pulse of electric current passed into the brain area under the electrode (see Figure 5–1). With some electrode placements this type of stimulation had no influence on the animal's lever-pressing. The animals simply continued to press the lever infrequently and indifferently as they moved about and explored the test cage. (The number of such spontaneous lever-presses which a

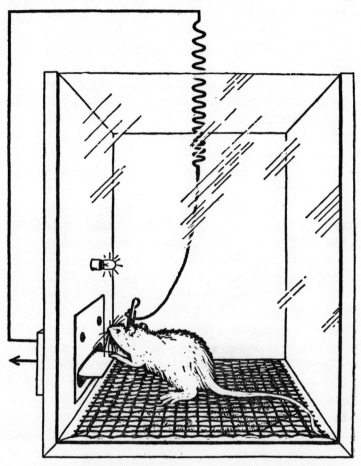

FIGURE 5–1.   Drawing of the type of experimental apparatus used to study self-stimulation of the brain in the rat. By depressing the lever extending into the cage at the left, the rat closes a circuit which supplies a brief burst of electric current to its brain through a wire connected to an electrode which is fixed to its skull. As indicated by the arrow at the left of the apparatus, the circuit which is activated by the lever is also connected to an automatic recorder which registers the rate at which the rat depresses the lever in order to receive the brain stimulation. (From James Olds, "Pleasure centers in the brain." *Scientific American,* 1956, **195**, no. 4, 105–116; reprinted with permission of the publisher.)

subject makes randomly in a specified time is called the *operant level* of responding.) With electrode placements in certain other parts of the brain, however, the rats learned to press the lever more and more rapidly until they reached a continuous high rate of responding. In this latter type of case, the intracranial stimulation acts as a positive reinforcement; when associated with the lever-pressing response, the stimulation leads to rates of responding which are dramatically higher than the operant level.

Delgado and his co-workers (1954) demonstrated that intracranial stimulation also could serve as a negative reinforcement. These experimenters tested cats in an apparatus consisting of two clearly different compartments separated by a removable partition. After showing that an animal had no inherent preference for either compartment, these workers confined it in one compartment and delivered stimulation to a part of the brain through a previously implanted electrode. Following several such stimulation trials, the cats showed external signs of fear when placed in the apparatus; the interior of the compartment had acquired the properties of a negative reinforcement. At this point in the training procedure, the investigators removed the partition between the two compartments and the cats quickly learned to escape from the one in which they had received the intracranial stimulation into the opposite one—even in the absence of further stimulation. This is the same thing that happens if a cat is shocked electrically in one compartment by electrodes on the floor on which it has to stand.

Investigators have also studied the negatively reinforcing effects of brain stimulation in the same lever-apparatus used to study positive reinforcement. In this case, however, the experimenter himself turns on the stimulating current and the animals must learn to turn it off by depressing the lever. They show rapid improvement in the promptness with which they rescue themselves when the electrode is implanted in one of the negatively reinforcing areas of the brain. Intracranial stimulation thus can serve as a primary negative reinforcement.

When intracranial stimulation serves as a punishment, the effect is not thought to be due to pain in the usual sense in which this word is used. For example, it is known from observing human subjects undergoing brain operations with only local anesthesia of the scalp that stimulation of the general substance of the brain itself does not give rise to feelings of pain. Therefore the behavior obtained by Delgado, Roberts, and Miller, for instance, cannot be the result of direct stimulation of pain receptors in the brain; it must be due to the stimulation of brain circuits that, in turn, mimic the action of a primary negative reinforcement. Nor do workers think that these punishment effects of stimulation are simply the result of the activation of pathways which normally carry sensory impulses from peripheral pain receptors. Such an explanation seems unlikely because, as we shall see, not all the parts of the brain involved systematically parallel known sensory pathways. Moreover, certain of the effects of electrically induced punishment are not identical with what would be expected from a simple painful experience.

Since the original discovery of these reinforcing systems in the brain, numerous experimenters have attempted to learn more about them. Probably no other single discovery concerned with brain function and behavior ever has led to more vigorous research activity by investigators in a number of scientific fields (Brady, 1961; Olds, 1962). The Skinner box already described has been most widely used in these studies for several reasons. One advantage to this method is the ease and rapidity with which experimental animals learn the manual manipulation by which they can initiate or terminate the brain stimulation. Many kinds of animal can manage the lever; a comparison between species is possible. While the rat has been most widely studied, cats and monkeys as well as fish can learn to manipulate some form of lever in order to obtain a reward.

Intracranial self-stimulation even has been studied by the same method in a few human patients in whom there was a medical reason for introducing electrodes into the brain. The few human studies, however, have not yet been very instructive since there is difficulty in evaluating the behavior of patients who are already suffering from some disease of the brain. Moreover, the electrodes, since they are being used for diagnosis in human patients, are not placed precisely to satisfy experimental requirements.

The use of a lever-press response also has the advantage that the rate of an experimental subject's responses can be accurately measured by recording each depression of the lever on a constantly moving tape. How rapidly the animal pushes the lever is considered to be an indication of the amount of reward derived from the brain stimulation; the more reward, the faster the animal works. Conversely, the investigator can determine the psychological intensity of a negatively reinforcing stimulation of the brain by noting, on the tape, how long it takes an animal to turn off the stimulating current.

Comparison of Intracranial Stimulation with External Rewards

Psychologists, interested in discovering laws that will help explain various patterns of learned behavior, have acquired during the past twenty-five years a great deal of information about the behavior of animals in the Skinner box when such standard external reinforcers as food, water, and electric shock are used. These findings provide a valuable background for comparison with the behavior patterns of animals motivated to lever-press for intracranial stimulation.

Behavioral scientists have compared these samples of behavior to see whether intracranial stimulation actually functions in the same way as more standard reinforcers. In the case of positively reinforced behavior (which has received the most research attention), this comparison reveals considerable similarity between the effects of external and intracranial reinforcers. For example, from a large number of experiments psychologists know that supplying external rewards according to different schedules can have a marked influence on the pattern of the lever-pressing responses. If a pellet of food, for instance, is delivered to an animal in a Skinner box only at irregular intervals, rather than each time the lever is pressed, the animal will continue to depress the lever steadily but at a much reduced rate; if a constant interval of reinforcement is used, the animal learns the time interval and responds more rapidly at about the time a reward is due. Alternatively, the Skinner box can be arranged so that a reward is delivered only after the occurrence of a particular number of lever-presses, such as after twenty, or even fifty, presses in a row; the animal responds at a very high rate with this type of reward schedule. Investigators who have similarly varied the schedule by which positively reinforcing stimulation of the brain is made available to experimental animals report that the pattern and rate of lever-pressing is modified in the same way. Results such as these suggest that, at least for the electrode placements so far studied, intracranial stimulation may be able to activate the same neural systems as those responsible for some of the behavioral effects of externally presented rewards.

Investigators also have discovered another clear similarity between the effects of intracranial stimulation and the effects of ordinary rewards in their study of a more complex motivational process, so-called *secondary reinforcement*. Psychologists use this term to refer to those circumstances in which a neutral stimulus, such as a novel tone, comes to have reinforcing characteristics, either positive or negative, after it has been paired with a primary reinforcer such as food or shock. This same sharing of reinforcement properties also occurs when electrical stimulation in a reward area of the brain is repeatedly paired with a neutral stimulus. Psychologists can demonstrate this motivational effect with a Skinner box that contains two separate levers. When the rat depresses one lever, a soft tone of one second's duration is sounded in the box; depressing the second lever has no effect at all. Since pressing these levers produces neither external nor intracranial reinforcement, the animal manipulates both of them only at a low operant level and shows no preference for depressing one more than the other. In a second stage of this experiment, however, with the levers removed from the box, the same soft tone is paired with electrical stimulation of one of the positively reinforcing areas in the brain. Then, when the two levers are again available and the brain stimulation has been terminated, experimental animals show an unmistakable preference for pushing the lever that presents them with the sound of the previously uninteresting tone.

Aside from the fact that the tone comes to function as a secondary reinforcement in the last part of the experiment, this behavior also shows that intracranial stimulation can increase an animal's lever-pressing rate even though the brain is *not* being stimulated at the time the animal is responding. This fact is important since it was suggested at first that the increased rate of lever-pressing in Olds's early work might have been due to some direct effect on the response systems of the brain. It then seemed possible that intracranially re-warded animals might simply be depressing the lever more rapidly as a compulsive, even convulsive, consequence of the stimulating current. Experimental findings like these con-cerned with secondary reinforcement appear to rule out this kind of explanation.

After demonstrating that intracranial stimulation can rein-force lever-pressing, investigators also showed that it has more general reinforcing properties. For example, if a rat is put into a test chamber in which the floor is marked off arbi-trarily into different areas, the animal will spend about equal amounts of time in each of the areas. There is no reason to be one place more than the other, so, once adjusted to the new environment, the animal wanders randomly about the box. Intracranial stimulation then is given each time the animal enters one particular area, and it is repeated at intervals as long as there is no movement out of that area. If the electrode is in a part of the brain from which positive reinforcement can be obtained, the animal will start to spend more and more time in the section of the box in which brain stimulation is supplied.

An animal also will learn to run faster to reach a place where intracranial stimulation is delivered. Workers have demonstrated this fact in a simple apparatus consisting of a straight alley with a starting box at one end and a goal box at the opposite end. The animal is allowed to run down the alley and enter the goal box, where an intracranial stimulation is delivered by the experimenter. If the brain stimulation is positively reinforcing, the animal soon starts to run with increasing speed from the starting box to the goal box. Experimenters also can measure how much an animal "likes" a particular brain stimulation by placing an electrified grid in the floor of the alley, one which must be crossed in order to get to the goal box and receive the stimulation. Rats will tolerate much larger shocks to their feet in return for rewarding stimulation of the brain than they will for food, even when they are very hungry. Under these experimental conditions, at least, animals apparently desire the intracranial stimulation more than life-sustaining nourishment. Such comparisons are difficult to make with certainty, but these researches do indeed indicate the effectiveness as well as the generality of the reinforcing properties of intracranial stimulation.

Animals also will learn and remember complex new patterns of behavior to obtain electric stimulation of certain parts of the brain. For example, rats will learn a complicated path through a maze to receive a reward of intracranial stimulation in the goal box just as rapidly as they will when they are hungry and there is food in the goal box. In some respects, animals that are working for brain stimulation in a maze perform even better than those being rewarded with food and water. Experimental results of the type we have been considering have led most behavioral scientists to conclude that Olds and Milner, in their original work, were indeed influencing circuits in the brain which are concerned with the psychological process of reinforcement.

Direct electrical stimulation of these reward systems in the brain, however, has some effects on behavior which are not identical with the effects of more natural external rewards. Monkeys, for instance, are seemingly unable to learn to press a lever at a very slow rate when working to obtain intracranial stimulation, but they learn to do it readily when a food reward is used. When highly rewarding intracranial stimulation is the reinforcement, the animals press the lever too often and, apparently, are unable to inhibit the lever-response between rewards even though when working at high speed they receive nothing in return for their extra work.

A similar inability to stop responding is seen when an investigator attempts to slow the rate of lever-pressing by frightening an experimental animal. Normally, if a thirsty rat is pressing a lever for a reward of water, the animal's activity will stop promptly when it hears a tone that has previously been paired with electric shock to its feet. The rat, having been conditioned for the paired tone's coming with the shock, acquires a fear of the tone and the conditioned fear suppresses the lever-pressing. This is called a *conditioned emotional response* and is discussed more fully in Chapter 6. Rats working for a reward of intracranial stimulation, however, do not react in this way. They continue to press the lever even when the tone is sounded. Psychologists believe that such perseveration of behavior means that the reinforcing properties of intracranial stimulation are so compelling that other events are relatively ineffective in changing the animal's behavior.

There is one additional respect in which investigators have found stimulation of the brain and external reinforcers surprisingly different. Animals appear to have difficulty remembering the rewarding nature of the intracranial stimulation. In the case of external rewards, for example, an animal has no trouble remembering for long periods of time the precise location of a source of food or water. When placed in a self-stimulation apparatus, however, investigators usually have to prime the animal by supplying one burst of intracranial stimulation before the subject starts to press the lever voluntarily. This is the case even though the animal is allowed self-stimulation in the same apparatus every day. By contrast, if the apparatus is arranged so that a lever-press releases food, a hungry animal will start pressing the lever immediately on being placed in the experimental apparatus.

This same type of difference is seen when animals are placed in a straight alleyway and required to run its length to obtain either a small bite of food or a rewarding stimulation of the brain which is gratuitously supplied by the experimenter. When the animals are kept waiting in the start box for longer and longer periods of time before being allowed to enter the alleyway, the animals that are running for food will run faster and faster. They appear, understandably enough, to get hungrier while they are waiting. This is not the case, however, with animals running to receive stimulation to their brain. As time is allowed to pass, they begin to run more slowly, as though they had begun to lose interest in reaching the other end of the alley. The reason for this difference is not yet understood. It may be that experimental animals have no frame of reference for remembering the unnatural feeling of pleasure associated with a rewarding intracranial stimulation. They have been eating all of their lives but have never received intracranial stimulation until they are brought into the laboratory as adult animals. Another possibility is that the artificial electrical stimulation may interfere directly with various brain circuits, disrupting neural activity that is essential to the fixation of memories.

Anatomy of Reinforcement Systems

The regions of the brain in which investigators can produce reinforcement by electrical stimulation are diagrammed for the rat in Figure 5–2. Four different kinds of area have been discovered. Electrodes in some areas produce only purely positive or only purely negative reinforcing effects. From other parts of the brain, usually adjacent to areas yielding pure motivational effects, investigators obtain ambivalent reinforcement. Depending on the type and duration of electrical current employed, stimulation of these ambivalent areas can give either positive or negative effects, or, sometimes, a combination of the two occur in sequence. Finally, there are many areas that have been explored only slightly, in which,

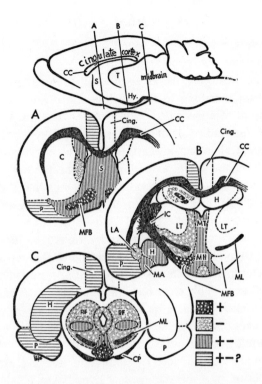

FIGURE 5–2. Diagrams of three different levels of the rat brain illustrating the location of areas found to have motivational properties in self-stimulation experiments. The levels of the three cross-sections are indicated on the medial view of the rat brain at the top. The key is shown at the bottom right: the plus sign means that an area has reward properties while the minus sign indicates that stimulation of an area is punishing to the animal. The vertical hatching (plus-minus) indicates areas in which both kinds of reinforcement have been observed. The lighter horizontal hatching signifies areas from which both effects have been elicited but have as yet been only sparsely studied. Since brain structures are symmetrical, some structures are labeled only on the right side of the cross-sections with shading only indicated on the left. Major fiber bundles are shown in black. (CC = corpus callosum; CP = cerebral peduncle; IC = internal capsule; ML = medial lemniscus; C = caudate nucleus; Cing. = cingulate gyrus; H = hippocampus; Hy. = hypothalamus; LA = lateral amygdala; LT = lateral thalamus; MA = medial amygdala; MFB = medial forebrain bundle; MH = medial hypothalamus; MT = medial thalamus; P = pyriform cortex; RF = reticular formation; S = septal area; T = thalamus. (Modified from M. E. Olds and James Olds, "Approach-avoidance analysis of rat diencephalon." *Journal of Comparative Neurology,* 1963, **120,** 259–315.)

nevertheless, workers have found some scattered instances of reinforcement (Olds and Olds, 1963).

For the most part, the areas in which stimulation produces reinforcement belong to the phylogenetically older parts of the brain or to areas closely connected with them. In all species thus far studied, stimulation produces purely positive reinforcement all along a nearly cylindrical path of tissue on each side of the brain, extending from the base of the forebrain down through the lateral hypothalamus into the ventral midbrain. This reward zone closely parallels the course of the medial forebrain bundle (MFB), an important tract that interconnects the rhinencephalon and various structures in the brainstem (see Figure 2–8). The portion of this reward zone in the lateral hypothalamus is a particularly potent area for reinforcement. With electrodes placed here, rats will stimulate themselves at rates as high as 8,000 lever-presses per hour and continue to do so for twenty-four hours or more until they finally drop from exhaustion. Clear positive reinforcement can also be produced by stimulating the subthalamus or the posterior part of the medial hypothalamus above the mammillary bodies, although these two areas are not present in the three selected cross-sections illustrated in Figure 5–2.

Animals stimulate themselves less vigorously when the electrodes are in the ambivalent areas (vertically hatched in Figure 5–2) that tend to surround the purely positive zones. Self-stimulation of these ambivalent areas, for the most part, is both less rapid and less persistent than in the case of the purely positive zones. Typically, these animals also appear to become satiated more promptly. With a stimulating electrode in the septal region, for example, response rates of less than 1,000 per hour are the rule, and the animals stop responding after only a few hours of self-stimulation. Extinction or cessation of the lever-pressing response also takes place relatively rapidly when the stimulating current to the septum is turned off. The ambivalent areas from which the weaker type of positive reinforcement can be obtained, in addition to the septal region, include parts of the caudate nucleus, the preoptic hypothalamic area, the medial hypothalamus, the medial thalamic regions, the medial amygdala, and parts of the midbrain reticular formation.

As already mentioned, investigators also find negative reinforcement resulting from stimulation in parts of the ambivalent areas when they use certain kinds of stimulating current. A good demonstration of such opposing effects from a single placement of an electrode is provided by experiments in which two levers are available to the animal. With certain placements of an electrode in the ambivalent areas, animals will turn on brain stimulation with one lever and then promptly turn it off again with the other, alternating these two responses indefinitely. It is as though a little bit of such stimulation is pleasant, while too much becomes unpleasant.

Positive reinforcement apparently can also be produced by stimulating some of the cortical areas which belong to the rhinencephalon and limbic system, as indicated by horizontal hatching in Figure 5–2. These areas in the telencephalon, however, have not yet been extensively studied with self-stimulation procedures, and relatively little is known about their reinforcing characteristics.

The effects obtained from this type of intracranial stimulation are influenced to a large extent by the characteristics of the stimulating current. The wave form, strength, and duration of the electrical stimulation all help determine the effectiveness and, with some electrode placements, the quality of the resulting reinforcement.

Investigators have not yet been able to find any clear relationship between the reinforcing characteristics of all these various brain areas and what is known about their behavioral function from other types of experiment. For example, parts

of both the caudate nucleus and the hippocampus are ambivalent areas, as judged by the effects of self-stimulation, but
they have little else in common so far as what is known otherwise about either their function or their anatomical connections. The lateral hypothalamus has seemed particularly puzzling in this regard. As you will remember from Chapter 3,
this lateral portion of the hypothalamus is thought to function
as an eating center. When an experimenter electrically stimulates the lateral hypothalamus, the stimulated animal starts to
eat if there is food available. It has seemed paradoxical,
therefore, that an animal would stimulate this area in itself
when such stimulation presumably induces hunger. Some
have argued that feelings of hunger are usually associated
with the subsequent reward of food consumption and that this
might explain the paradox.

The lateral hypothalamus, of course, is not anatomically
homogeneous. It contains many nerve cells as well as an
abundance of fiber paths, coursing both anteriorly and posteriorly. Accordingly, some investigators feel that the two different effects that can be produced by stimulating the lateral hypothalamus are the result of activating two different systems
within the area. As we have seen, the anterior–posterior dis-
tribution of this reward zone suggests, for one thing, that it
might be related to some system of fibers included in the medial forebrain bundle which passes through the lateral hypothalamus (see Figure 5–2). Conversely perhaps, the induction of eating could be dependent on other fiber systems or
local cell bodies.

While research workers have been less active in the study
of negatively reinforcing areas of the brain than in the case of
the reward areas, there is sufficient evidence to leave no doubt
that intracranial stimulation of certain parts of the brain can
function purely as does punishment. With stimulating electrodes implanted in an area of purely negative reinforcement,

experimental animals never attempt to turn the current on although, if the current is turned on by the experimenter, the animal learns promptly to press a lever in order to stop the intracranial stimulation and escape from the punishment. Such escape behavior is not limited to lever-pressing; animals will also run through a maze or shuttle back and forth between two experimental compartments to escape from the stimulation of these negatively reinforcing areas.

As with stimulation of the reward areas, animals also are capable of learning to anticipate this kind of punishment and can learn a specified response which enables them to avoid the stimulation. For example, rats will learn to press a lever when a warning tone is sounded in order to interrupt the stimulating circuit before their brain is stimulated. To the extent that investigators have studied it, intracranial stimulation of negatively reinforcing areas appears to mimic closely the effect of externally applied punishments.

The locations of the main negative reinforcement areas in the brain also are shown for the rat in Figure 5–2. The largest punishment areas are in the midbrain, within the reticular formation and the central gray substance which closely surrounds the medially placed aqueduct, and in the ventromedial portions of the thalamus. More particularly, the main thalamic nuclei which yield negative reinforcement are the reticular nucleus and the midline nucleus, both being part of the thalamic portion of the ascending reticular formation. In addition, investigators have reported negative reinforcement following stimulation of parts of the medial caudate nucleus, areas in the dorsal hippocampus, the lateral amygdala, and the ventral surface of the hypothalamus near the stalk of the pituitary gland. Although not included in the selected cross-sections shown in Figure 5–2, stimulation of the fornix tract, which connects the hippocampus with the posterior hypothalamus (see Figure 2–8), also has punishing effects.

As in the case of the reward areas, it is not well understood why all of these brain structures should be involved in negative reinforcement. In some instances there is a close association with sensory pathways (e.g., the medial lemniscus) which might account for the negative reinforcement. Moreover, in other of these brain areas, such as the lateral amygdala, stimulation is known to produce behavior which is clearly aversive, such as fighting or fleeing—behavior which is compatible with the negatively reinforcing effects of stimulation. On the basis of what is otherwise known about the brain, however, scientists have no ready explanation of why stimulation of such areas as the medial caudate nucleus, the dorsal hippocampus, or the fornix should influence an animal's behavior in the same way external punishment does.

6

BEHAVIORAL CONTRIBUTIONS OF THE LIMBIC SYSTEM

THE LIMBIC SYSTEM is an interconnected group of brain structures located mostly in the rhinencephalon, the most primitive portion of the cerebral hemispheres. The structures of the limbic system which are located here in the forebrain include the cingulate gyrus, the septal area, the amygdala, and the hippocampus (see Figure 2–6). The entorhinal cortex is also considered part of the limbic system because of its numerous connections with the hippocampus. Because of the connections between some of these centers in the rhinencephalon and restricted parts of the thalamus and hypothalamus, portions of these latter areas also are regarded as belonging to the limbic system. Figure 2–9 illustrates the connections among these various parts of the limbic system. Recent anatomical studies have demonstrated, moreover, that nerve fibers from some of the limbic structures in the rhinencephalon also extend directly back into the reticular system in the midbrain. It has therefore been suggested that this part of the brainstem should also be considered part of the limbic system. Clearly, the limbic system is spread widely throughout the brain, although not all of its anatomical connections are as yet understood.

The modern growth of interest in the limbic system's contributions to behavior did not stem from the anatomical discovery of its component parts or their connections. These were recognized, for the most part, many years ago. In fact, the recently coined term *limbic system* was derived from the older anatomical term *grand lobe limbique,* first suggested in 1878 by the French surgeon Paul Broca. His original term described the fact that these structures in the rhinencephalon form a border (*limbus*) around the junction between the diencephalon and forebrain (see Figure 2–6).

Not only are the various parts of the limbic system connected in a network of well-defined pathways; they also have wide connections, both sensory and motor, with many other parts of the central nervous system. For example, it seems likely that information from all the senses is capable of influencing electrical events within the limbic system. The changes in the brain waves associated with behavioral arousal have, moreover, been recorded widely throughout the limbic system as a result of stimulation in various parts of the ascending reticular system. A number of connections also exist between various structures in the limbic system and the neocortex, two-way connections which allow influences to operate in both directions. There are also pathways for motor outflow from the various parts of the limbic system. These pathways are not yet clearly identified, but there is no doubt that they exist. Indeed, one of the consistent results of electrical stimulation in certain centers of the limbic system is the production of autonomic responses and the modulation of body movements.

We may well ask why investigators have regarded the limbic system as forming a functionally separate system at all when it has so many connections with other parts of the brain. For one reason, the parts of the limbic system that lie within the rhinencephalon have been closely related anatomically almost since the beginning of vertebrate evolution. Moreover, some of the connections between parts of the limbic system are not only very old phylogenetically but are so prominent structurally that earlier workers suspected that a special functional relationship must exist between these brain structures. A good example of such a conspicuous connection is the large fornix bundle that connects the hippocampus with the hypothalamic portion of the limbic system (see figures 2–8 and 2–9). More recently, theories and experiments related to the limbic system's role in behavior have also suggested that, in some degree, the various limbic structures share some common function, but the suspicion remains at present unconfirmed.

Anatomists supposed originally that the rhinencephalon was concerned exclusively with the sense of smell, a conclusion that seemed to them likely because the nerves that carry sensory information from the smell receptors in the nose to the brain project directly into the front of the rhinencephalon. (*Rhinencephalon* means "nose-brain.") The point of view that the rhinencephalon functioned only as an olfactory center persisted until the late 1930s, despite C. Judson Herrick's earlier suggestions to the contrary. Herrick, one of the most respected neuroanatomists of his time, was impressed by the fact that the rhinencephalon received sensory information from modalities other than the olfactory system. Furthermore, he pointed to the multitude of connections that exist between the various centers in the rhinencephalon and other parts of the nervous system, particularly the neocortex. It seemed to him that this primitive part of the forebrain must perform more complex functions than the simple analysis of odors. From his knowledge of the comparative anatomy of the brain, he suggested that the rhinencephalon might be concerned with memory processes and emotionally motivated behavior (Herrick, 1933). Unheeded, he thus anticipated by many years the modern point of view about this part of the nervous system.

The present interest in the limbic system's role in behavior can be traced for the most part back to two scientific events in 1937. It was then that James W. Papez, a neuroanatomist, published his now-classic article which called attention to the connections between certain centers in the rhinencephalon (cingulate gyrus and hippocampus) and parts of the thalamus and hypothalamus. These structures and their interconnections have since become known as *Papez' circuit* (see Figure 2–9). Papez suggested that activity in this circuit might provide the neural basis for emotional experiences. He based his suggestion on clinical experience with patients who had suffered damage to this part of the brain and also considered the few examples of experimental work with animals which were available at that time. For example, physiologist Philip Bard had already demonstrated that an intact hypothalamus was necessary for the occurrence of the patterned behavior of rage in the cat (Bard, 1929).

Shortly after Papez published his paper, a pair of Chicago investigators, Heinrich Klüver and Paul C. Bucy, described the remarkable changes in behavior that result from bilateral removal of the tips of the temporal lobes in monkeys (Klüver and Bucy, 1939). Their operation also damaged those structures of the limbic system which are within the temporal lobe: the amygdala, the entorhinal cortex, and the ventral part of the hippocampus. This surgical damage produced a dramatic series of behavioral abnormalities that have come to be known as the Klüver-Bucy syndrome. Their monkeys were no longer particular about what they ate; they would even eat meat, which is not accepted normally by monkeys. They seemed unable to recognize even familiar objects in their cages. They would pick up things that were lying on the floor of the cage, finger them endlessly, test them in their mouths, and then drop them back onto the floor. A short while later they would examine the objects all over again in the same way, as though they were something new. These animals with damage to their temporal lobes were also hypersexual and were distinctly tamer and safer to handle than before the operation. The tameness that resulted from the brain ablation was of particular interest, since it seemed possible that the portion of the brain lesion which affected the limbic structures might have produced this behavioral change. Because the increased tameness seemed to constitute a change in the emotional status of these wild macaque monkeys, this finding was taken as supporting Papez' idea that structures in the limbic system can be important for emotional behavior. These two reports in the late 1930s stimulated wide research interest in both the physiological characteristics and the behavioral contributions of what has since come to be known as the limbic system.

Physiological Functions of the Limbic System

Neurophysiologists report a number of detailed effects that follow stimulation of the various limbic centers in the rhinencephalon. Which effects occur depend not only on the precise location of the stimulating electrode but are also determined by such conditions as the type of anesthesia used on the experimental animal, the depth of anesthesia during the experiment, and the physical characteristics of the electrical current applied to the brain. The physiological effects of stimulation vary quite markedly, for example, with small variations in the voltage, amperage, frequency, waveform, or duration of the electrical stimulus. The number of detailed findings from such physiological studies far exceed the present ability of scientists to relate them meaningfully to behavior. The major findings, however, follow some general patterns that can be described briefly. As we shall see later, the contrast between the effects of stimulation and the results of lesions in the same limbic structures suggests, in a very general way, one kind of role in behavior that the limbic system may play.

With the exception of the hippocampus, which will be considered separately, stimulation throughout these limbic areas in the rhinencephalon leads to a wide variety of autonomic changes. Blood pressure may be elevated or reduced; respiration may be speeded up, slowed down, or changed in amplitude; movements of the walls of the stomach and the intestine can either be increased or decreased. Electrical stimulation not only produces such changes from points widely spread throughout these brain centers, but can produce very diverse effects from points which are closely intermingled. In some areas, for example, moving the stimulating electrode by less than a millimeter will change the effect of stimulation from elevation to reduction of blood pressure or alter the autonomic response from salivation to erection of the hairs on the body. The rhinencephalon is apparently not organized in relation to particular autonomic systems or to the part of the body involved, or even to whether the response is sympathetic or parasympathetic. This situation is strikingly different from what occurs in the hypothalamus where, as we have seen, a clearer degree of anatomical organization exists according to specific autonomic systems and functions. In the hypothalamus, as we have seen, there is even an approximate division between sympathetic and parasympathetic processes. In the limbic centers, by contrast, there is a clear intermingling of points that can produce a wide variety of autonomic changes throughout the body.

Stimulation throughout the limbic part of the forebrain also can have a modifying influence on movements of the limbs and trunk. This influence, even with the electrode kept on one place, seems to apply equally to movements of all parts of the body. It thus appears that parts of these limbic centers can modify all types of somatomotor response pattern. Physiologists study this type of motor effect by stimulating limbic structures at the same time the response of a muscle is taking place and observing how the movement is modified by the stimulation of the brain. Only certain kinds of movement can be observed in these experiments, however, since the animals are anesthetized during such studies. For instance, spontaneous movements (like shaking and shivering) occur in anesthetized animals if the level of anesthesia is not too deep. Moreover, the experimenter can produce reflex movements by properly manipulating the limbs, or he can induce a variety of body movements by electrically stimulating specific motor centers in the brain—for instance, the motor areas in the neocortex. Physiological studies of this type show that parts of the limbic system can either *inhibit* or *facilitate* patterns of movement. The points which produce these opposing effects on the animal's activities are spread widely throughout the rhinencephalon. Certain circumscribed areas, however, show a predominance of one effect over the other. For example, a Norwegian neurophysiologist, Birger R. Kaada, who has contributed much to our understanding of these brain areas in the rhinencephalon, has shown that parts of the cingulate gyrus and amygdala have primarily a facilitatory effect on the animal's responses, while a zone of concentrated inhibitory points is located in the subcallosal area, which lies just in front of the septal area (Kaada, 1960). Inhibition of movements can also be produced by stimulating parts of the septal area itself.

Stimulation of some of these parts of the limbic system not only can modify response patterns that are already in progress, as just described, but can also produce limited patterns of movement. The patterns that result from limbic stimulation are typically gross and primitive, slow in onset and execution. They are usually diffuse tonic movements which persist throughout the period of stimulation. Commonly the movement produced by electrical stimulation in limbic structures is *contraversive*—the movement tends to orient a standing animal away from the side of the brain being stimulated.

In the case of the cingulate gyrus of the monkey at least, there is an organization of body movements according to specific parts of the body. Stimulation of the most anterior part of the monkeys' cingulate gyrus leads to gross movements of head and face; farther back in this gyrus, the head, shoulders, and upper extremities become active together and, with stimulation even more posterior, head, shoulders, upper extremities, and trunk all begin to move at once. The same differentiated pattern of movement repeats itself, in reverse, as the electrode is moved farther back in the cingulate gyrus.

Stimulation of the various limbic structures produces such a wide range of autonomic and somatomotor responses that it is surprising to discover that surgical damage to these same brain centers leads to no obvious loss in the animal's general motor ability. Animals with bilateral damage in one or another of these limbic areas move about and use their extremities in a perfectly normal manner. Furthermore, such autonomic functions as digestion and the control of the heart and blood pressure are not disrupted in any apparent way. This lack of obvious abnormality is far different, for instance, from the striking disorders of autonomic function that follow lesions in certain parts of the hypothalamus or the awkwardness and even paralysis that result from damage to the primary motor centers in the neocortex. In these latter parts of the brain, the effects of stimulation and the results of ablation clearly match each other. In the limbic system, however, the very functions that are so clearly modified by electrical stimulation do not deteriorate in any obvious way after severe surgical damage of the same structures.

Pierre Gloor, an investigator in Canada, has called attention to the possible meaning of this paradox (Gloor, 1960). He points out that these limbic structures are clearly able to influence parts of the brain that are concerned with visceral adjustments and body movements but, in view of the absence of motor disability following surgical lesions, they apparently do not contain cells that normally initiate such responses. Gloor suggests rather that these limbic centers, through their ability to inhibit and facilitate responses, may function to select response sequences that are appropriate to the needs of the moment. Physiological experiments, however, do not suggest under what psychological circumstances this selection of responses would be active. As we shall see, some answers to this question are provided by considering the limbic functions that have been discovered through the use of sensitive tests of behavior.

Stimulation of the hippocampus, in contrast to stimulation of the structures we have just considered, produces few observable effects despite the relatively large size of the hippocampus, its structural complexity, and the prominent connections it has with the rest of the limbic system and with other parts of the brain. A number of investigators have stimulated the hippocampus in anesthetized animals, but they have reported few observable effects—some minor changes in respiration or variations in the size of the pupil of the eye. Paul D.

MacLean, who stresses the importance of the hippocampus and related parts of the limbic system in mating behavior, reports additionally that erection of the male sex organ can be produced by stimulation of the hippocampus as well as at other places in the limbic system (MacLean, 1960). The relative paucity of observable effects when the hippocampus is stimulated in the anesthetized animal suggests that it may be involved in complex brain activity not directly connected either with the actual selection or initiation of autonomic or somatomotor responses. We shall shortly examine some behavioral studies that partly support this expectation.

Behavioral Effects of
Limbic Stimulation

Electrical stimulation of certain centers in the limbic system through permanently implanted electrodes produces clear effects on the behavior of unanesthetized animals. One effect, the so-called *attention response,* can be induced by stimulation in many of the limbic structures in the rhinencephalon. Following such stimulation, the animal first stops abruptly and stands still with its head raised and, as the stimulation continues, opens its eyes widely, the pupils dilate, and the ears begin to move as though to pick up some slight sound. Finally, if the stimulation continues, the animal glances about quickly with coordinated movements of the head and eyes. Most commonly the head and eye movements are primarily toward the side opposite the side of stimulation. During this attention response, the animal is usually responsive to whatever is happening in the environment and looks like a normal animal that is alertly searching its surroundings.

Throughout this response sequence, the animal appears to be quite aroused, an effect which fits well with the intimate connection that exists between the limbic system and the ascending reticular system. In fact, the electrical stimulation which produces the attention response also typically produces desynchronization of the EEG which, as we have already noted, is the brain-wave pattern characteristic of alert or aroused animals. Stimulation in those limbic areas that inhibit body movements very commonly leads to the attention response. This is of interest because the inhibition of ongoing behavior is always seen at the beginning of the attention response.

Electrical stimulation in certain parts of the limbic system also can produce fully integrated patterns of behavior in the awake animal that seem identical with the behavior in normally occurring flight and defense. Stimulation of parts of the hypothalamus can lead to similar responses, as we have already seen. These elaborate responses are obtained from more restricted parts of the rhinencephalon than is the simpler attention response. The responses of flight and defense occur primarily with stimulation of the amygdala, although flight can also be initiated by stimulating the anterior part of the cingulate gyrus.

The behavior of flight or defense in these stimulated animals may be produced in a mild abbreviated form or, by increasing the strength and duration of the electrical stimulation to the brain, the total response pattern can be elicited. The amount of electrical stimulation thus seems able to mimic the intensity of emotional arousal in the normal occurrence of these instinctive response patterns. In the flight response, the stimulated animal first shows the attention response already described. The animal then crouches and begins to withdraw as though from some dangerous adversary. Finally, if the stimulating current is further increased, the animal suddenly turns and starts into full flight. It will even attempt to hide, if a suitable place is available. In the defense response, the sequence of behavior develops from simple attention to crouching, hissing, growling, and finally it culminates in striking with the bared claws in outright attack.

Experimenters are not fully agreed on whether the control of the responses for flight and defense is spread diffusely throughout the amygdala or organized into separate systems. There is good reason to believe, however, that there are separate but overlapping zones in the amygdala for the control of these two kinds of emotional behavior. Stimulation of the amygdala also is reported to produce sniffing, licking, and swallowing in unanesthetized animals.

These results of brain stimulation in animals have been partly confirmed by observing surgical patients who are conscious during brain operations. In such patients, electrical stimulation in the cingulate gyrus or near the amygdala is reported to result in vague feelings of fear. Furthermore, epileptic patients with electrical abnormalities in the area of the amygdala sometimes experience bouts of fear or attacks of rage in connection with their epileptic attacks. All of these results from studies of brain stimulation support the conclusion that, whatever else it may do, parts of the limbic system are involved in some way with emotional behavior.

Changes in Emotionality
Following Limbic Lesions

A number of investigators have reported two dramatic changes in behavior that occur following surgical damage to parts of the limbic system. These changes represent alterations in the general emotional behavior of the operated animals: lesions in the amygdala or cingulate cortex can tame an otherwise wild animal, while surgical damage to parts of the septum produces vicious rage in the operated animals.

Klüver and Bucy first reported that monkeys become tamer after large temporal-lobe lesions. At that time, the investigators were not sure which of the several brain structures involved in the lesions was responsible for this change in behavior. It is now known, however, that lesions restricted mainly to the amygdala will produce docility in wild animals. This result has been observed in monkeys, in nondomesticated cats, and even in the very wild lynx. Wildcats, for instance, too ferocious to be handled without nets and protective gloves can be safely petted following bilateral ablation of the appropriate part of the amygdala. Furthermore, when monkeys are tamed in this way and then put back with their normal cagemates, the social relationships within the group undergo a change. The experimental animals fall to a lower level in the social scale; they play a more submissive role than they did before they were operated on. Surgical damage to the anterior cingulate gyrus also produces placidity, but the effect is apparently not so striking as after lesions in the amygdala.

A few experimenters also have found that damage in the area of the amygdala can result in heightened irritability or increased ferociousness, which is of course the opposite of the effect we have just considered. It is not yet understood how lesions in the same brain center can lead to such opposite effects on behavior. As we have seen, however, stimulation of the amygdala shows that it may contain at least two different behavioral systems. It may be that this lesion can produce these two opposite effects on emotional behavior by damaging these two systems or nearby structures to differing degrees.

Surgical damage to the septum also produces a remarkable change in the general emotional behavior of animals. The resulting abnormality in behavior is called the *septal rage syndrome*. Investigators most commonly have studied this syndrome in the rat, since this species shows the changes of behavior in a very exaggerated form, although septal rage can be produced in other species as well. A laboratory rat that is normally gentle becomes a wild and aggressive beast following this kind of brain lesion. The operated rat viciously attacks other rats as well as the hand of an unwary experimenter. Such animals are extremely hyperirritable. An unexpected sound or even a gentle tap on the back leads to an exaggerated startle response; the rat may spring twelve inches straight up into the air, screeching loudly all the time, and land on the floor prepared for an immediate attack on anything in sight. However, if such rats are kept in an ordinary colony room for animals, exposed to daily stimulation from neighboring animals, and occasionally manipulated carefully by the investigator, the rage largely subsides in about two weeks. In isolated rats, on the other hand, the rage pattern is not so short-lived. It is not yet known how long the septal rage syndrome would persist in totally isolated animals.

This pattern of rage can be duplicated by a lesion in part of the hypothalamus and counteracted by an amygdala lesion of the sort that tames normally wild animals. Conversely, a placid, amygdalectomized cat can be made vicious by damage to the rage area in the hypothalamus. These three subcortical areas (septum, amygdala, and hypothalamus) are connected by well-known anatomical pathways, but behavioral scientists do not yet understand how they function together in the normal control of aggressive behavior.

Effect of Limbic Lesions
on Fear-Motivated Behavior

Behavioral scientists, attempting to quantify systematically the effects of limbic lesions on emotional behavior, have studied almost exclusively the performance of fear-motivated animals. The reason for this concentration of effort is simple: These workers can be sure they have frightened an animal in an experimental test but they do not have the techniques for the reliable induction of other emotional states under controlled laboratory conditions. In general, the tests in common use are arranged so that, on a given signal, the animals know they will soon receive a brief electric shock from the bars of the floor of the test apparatus. During the period when they are anticipating the shock-punishment, they are assumed to be frightened and their general behavior supports this assumption. Under such an experimental condition animals may vocalize loudly, scratch wildly at the floor, or crouch tensely. The erratic shifts in heart rate and breathing pattern, commonly seen in these circumstances, also are indicative of a frightened animal.

Investigators usually have concentrated on certain specific measurements in their studies of fear-motivated behavior. For instance, they observe how many times a prior warning signal (such as a tone) must be presented along with the electric shock before the animal learns to be frightened by the tone without the shock. Once this learning has taken place, the animal can learn to jump consistently into an adjoining safe compartment whenever the warning tone is sounded and thus avoid being shocked. This learned behavior is called a *conditioned avoidance response* (CAR). Experimenters commonly measure the number of training trials before the animal has fully acquired the CAR, thus obtaining what is called an *acquisition score*. Once a subject has learned the CAR, the tone can be presented without the shock, and the number of trials until the animal stops responding to the tone then provides a measure of how long it takes for an animal to lose or extinguish its fear of the tone. This latter measure is called an *extinction score*.

Two different kinds of conditioned avoidance response have been used in studies of the limbic system: the *active* avoidance response and the *passive* avoidance response. When experimental animals must actively make a response in order to avoid punishment, as with the CAR just described, they are performing an active avoidance response. By contrast, a passive avoidance response is when an animal suppresses or inhibits a normally occurring response in order to avoid punishment. For example, hungry cats that learn to inhibit their approach to a dish of food where previously they have been shocked are displaying passive avoidance behavior. They are avoiding further punishment passively by not responding.

Under certain conditions, animals will stop whatever they are doing and crouch motionless when they are frightened. Laboratory investigators have also studied the effect of brain lesions on this type of fear-induced response, which they call a *conditioned emotional response* (CER). This type of behavior is studied in the laboratory by presenting, for instance, a tone which is followed by an *unavoidable* electric shock to the feet of the animal. The tone and shock are repeated until the tone becomes a potent danger signal for the animal. The tone is then sounded while the animal is performing some other task, like manipulating a lever to obtain food, and the degree to which the tone suppresses the animal's performance with the lever provides a quantitative measurement of the CER.

Sometimes a brain lesion is made before the animal is studied on such tests as these; in this case the experimenter is studying the effect of the lesion on the acquisition of the performance of these various fear-motivated patterns of behavior. In other studies, the experimental animals are trained to perform correctly before the brain operation. They are tested after the surgery to see whether their ability to perform the task is still retained or whether the brain lesions have disrupted the *retention* of the fear-motivated response that was learned prior to the operation.

Following Papez' suggestions, investigators reasoned at first that damage to the various limbic centers should produce subjects that were less easily frightened than normal animals and, accordingly, these brain-damaged subjects were expected to do poorly on all the types of behavior test that we have just considered. Many limbic lesions have been studied in this manner, but we shall look first at the effects of cingulate and septal lesions, since they have received the most study and they also provide a model by which we can then briefly consider the effects of other types of limbic damage on fear-motivated behavior. In general, either cingulate or septal damage does produce abnormalities of fear-motivated behavior, providing the ablation is a bilateral; for the lesion to be effective, a structure must be damaged on both sides of the brain. This appears to be the case for all the behavioral effects of all limbic lesions.

Animals with bilateral cingulate damage, for instance, take many more trials than normal animals to learn to make an active avoidance response when a warning signal is presented, and some of these operated animals are totally incapable of learning a CAR. Furthermore, some reports indicate that the same limbic lesions which disrupt the learning of an active avoidance response also lead to rapid extinction of such a learned response when the warning signal is presented repeatedly without the punishing shock. It seems that these brain-damaged animals, once they have finally learned to avoid punishment, get over their fear quite promptly when they are no longer punished with the shock. Septally damaged animals, under circumstances in which normal subjects show vigorous passive avoidance, also are found to be deficient. Septal animals seemingly cannot hold themselves back from a potentially dangerous source of food or water. They also fail to develop a CER in a normal manner; instead of crouching tensely in response to the warning signal, as normal animals do under such test conditions, the septal animal simply continues to perform whatever task is at hand. Thus we see that certain types of fear-motivated behavior are clearly disrupted following damage to either the cingulate or septal areas. Earlier workers were puzzled to find that such brain-damaged animals, impaired on certain of these tests, were normal on others. Cingulate lesions produce no deficit in passive avoidance nor are such operated animals impaired in the performance of a CER. Conversely, septal lesions never disrupt active-avoidance behavior.

The different physiological results of electrical stimulation in these limbic structures suggest how these apparent inconsistencies in the effects of cingulate and septal lesions on fear-motivated behavior can be understood. As already pointed out, certain limbic centers *facilitate* autonomic and somatomotor responses while other limbic structures *inhibit* such responses. It so happens that much of the cingulate gyrus is primarily a facilitatory area, while the limbic cortex anterior of the cingulate gyrus (subcallosal cortex) along with the adjacent septum are powerful inhibitory areas. The behavioral experiments we have just considered show that both of these limbic areas are important for fear-motivated behavior, but, more significantly, the behavior studies show that an intact *facilitatory* area is necessary for normal *active* avoidance behavior, while the *inhibitory* area must be intact if *passive* avoidance behavior and the ability to perform a CER are to remain normal.

The areas concerned in these studies are diagrammed in Figure 6–1. Damage to the facilitatory area in the cingulate

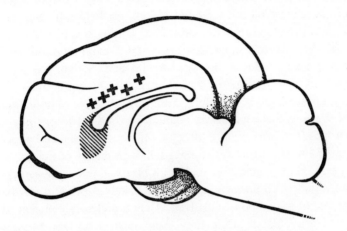

FIGURE 6–1. Schematic diagram of a medial view of the cat's brain showing two areas of the limbic system in which electrical stimulation leads to modification of motor responses. The plus signs indicate a motor *facilitatory* area; the hatched zone, overlapping subcallosal and septal areas, is a motor *inhibitory* zone. Lesions within either of these two areas produce a deficit in fear-motivated behavior. The type of deficit matches the response modulating function of each area. See text for further description. (Modified from R. A. McCleary, "Response specificity in the behavioral effects of limbic system lesions in the cat." *Journal of Comparative and Physiological Psychology*, 1961, **54**, 605–613; reprinted with permission of the publisher.)

gyrus disrupts avoidance behavior only when the operated animal is required to make an active response (such as jumping or running) in order to avoid punishment. Conversely, damage to the area having a predominant inhibitory influence disrupts only those tasks requiring the operated animal to inhibit or suppress its responses. Damage to other inhibitory areas in the brain, for example to parts of temporal neocortex, to the anterior hypothalamus, and to the medial caudate nucleus, also disrupts an animal's ability to avoid punishment passively.

Such an analysis, according to the type of avoidance response required of the animal, also helps make sense of some of the effects of other limbic lesions on behavior. For instance, investigators have found that cutting one of the main pathways to the cingulate gyrus (the mammillo-thalamic tract) also produces an experimental animal that has difficulty in learning how to avoid shock-punishment actively by running to a place of safety. Similarly, electrical stimulation of the amygdala has more facilitatory than inhibitory effect on motor responses and, fittingly, impaired avoidance behavior following lesions in the amygdala is primarily of the active type. Finally, whether animals with hippocampal damage perform poorly on an avoidance test is strictly dependent on the nature of the response involved. They are clearly deficient at passive avoidance while they even outstrip normal animals when required actively to avoid punishment. This result was not to be expected following hippocampal damage, since neurophysiologists so far have uncovered neither facilitatory nor inhibitory motor functions in this large limbic structure.

Some investigators have emphasized the fact that two of the limbic areas that have motor facilitatory functions, the cingulate gyrus and the amygdala, are also centers from which flight responses can be initiated by electrical stimulation. With this fact in mind, it has been suggested that the active avoidance deficit which follows lesions in these areas may represent an impaired ability to initiate flight during the avoidance test. Along the same lines, other investigators feel that these brain-damaged animals are deficient at avoiding shock actively because their natural tendency to "freeze" in response to punishment becomes exaggerated after the neural basis of the flight response is disrupted. These alternative interpretations are still concerned with motor facilitatory and motor inhibitory processes, but they emphasize the possibility that limbic lesions may interfere with the innate patterns of response that are required by particular experimental tests.

In marked contrast to these points of view is the suggestion that impaired passive-avoidance behavior, following septal lesions for example, is actually due to increased hunger or thirst produced by the brain damage. According to this way of looking at the matter, the operated animals are pulled back to the potentially punishing reward because they have a stronger need for it; they are not, so to speak, forced back because they are unable to stop themselves. It is apparently true that some limbic lesions, notably in the septum and parts of the amygdala, do produce changes in appetite, or at least in the amount eaten or drunk. It is now known, however, that septal animals show the same impairment in their ability to avoid punishment passively even in special passive-avoidance tests that involve neither a food nor a water reward.

The effect of limbic lesions on the performance of fear-motivated responses learned prior to the surgical damage is not clearly established. The experiments concerned with this problem are called retention studies because the investigator is concerned with whether the animal retains the ability to perform the task despite the intervening brain lesion. As a general rule, nervous system lesions that disrupt the learning of a particular type of response also disrupt its performance when the animal is lesioned after having been trained on the task. An interesting exception to this general rule is the fact that hippocampal lesions interfere with the retention of a previously learned *active* avoidance response while such lesioned animals have no trouble learning such a response in the first place. As we shall see, however, there is reason to think that the hippocampus plays a special role in the maintenance of recent memory.

A general point about limbic function becomes clear when one considers all these findings together. No specific limbic center appears to be crucial for fear-motivated behavior in general, contrary to what might have been expected from Papez' early suggestions. Whether a particular structure in the limbic system is behaviorally important at any particular time is apparently dependent on the detailed characteristics of the performance which the circumstances require of the organism.

Effect of Limbic Lesions
on Complex Behavior and Memory

The amygdala contributes to psychological abilities that are more complex than flight and defense responses or the facilitation of avoidance behavior. For instance, monkeys with bilateral damage to the amygdala have trouble solving complicated visual problems when required to solve them in order to receive a small reward of food. These animals can solve simple visual problems as well as normal animals can, but they are deficient when they must generalize what they have learned to new visual patterns that are similar, but not identical, to the original patterns they learned to distinguish. These brain-damaged monkeys also have difficulty when they must reverse a learned habit and select a visual pattern that previously was not the correct choice. Following lesions of the amygdala, these animals may have difficulty when a visual problem is altered in some way simply because they cannot habituate themselves easily to any kind of novel situation.

This possibility is suggested by the fact that such brain-damaged monkeys persist in exploring and re-exploring new surroundings and accordingly remain hyperactive long after normal monkeys have become calm and well adapted to the same novel environment.

The inability to handle complex visual problems following damage to the amygdala does not seem to correlate with many of the other effects we already have considered in connection with the amygdala. On the other hand, this limbic structure is composed of many separate parts, and there is no reason to expect a homogeneous function for the entire structure.

Cats with septal lesions, working for a food reward, are also deficient at solving a visual problem if the experimenter complicates it by reversing the original positions of the correct and incorrect test objects. In the case of septal damage, this deficit seems understandable, for we already have seen with respect to passive avoidance that such lesioned animals have great difficulty in suppressing a suddenly inappropriate learned response. It is of special interest that septal cats show this same type of impairment on a test in which no shock-punishment is used. Apparently the various abnormalities of fear-motivated behavior, following limbic damage, are not all necessarily limited to such samples of "emotional" behavior.

The possible role of the hippocampus in memory has attracted the interest of many investigators. This role was first suspected from the abnormality of neurological patients who had bilateral damage to the hippocampus as the result of either surgery or disease. Such patients have great difficulty in storing memory records of new events as they occur. The defect in recent memory, however, is relative rather than absolute. Some new memories can still be acquired, although their acquisition usually takes prolonged exposure to the new material and conscientious practice. Without repetitious practice, these patients are able to remember something new only as long as they "keep their mind on it." Once their attention turns to a subsequent event, the memory of the preceding one is apt to vanish.

In addition to this deficit in recent memory, there is a second kind of memory defect, *retrograde amnesia,* that extends back in time for a variable period prior to the occurrence of the hippocampal damage. The retrograde amnesia may cover only a few previous months or it may affect a year. Memory for events that took place before the amnesic period, however, as well as old well-established motor skills, are perfectly remembered. For example, a person with hippocampal damage has great difficulty remembering the number of his current hospital room, but he can easily remember his childhood street address. Moreover, he is able to play his usual game of tennis provided he learned to play before the period of retrograde amnesia. Tests show that the mental ability of these patients is otherwise normal. They show no deficiency in general intelligence, vocabulary, or the ability to concentrate and reason.

How the hippocampus contributes to the normal functioning of memory is not known. It may convert new information into a type of neural code suitable for memory storage, or it may store such coded information temporarily. Possibly it helps reactivate recently stored memories when a person attempts to recall events in the near past.

One neurophysiological study, however, has demonstrated a type of electrical change that takes place in the hippocampal area of the cat's brain when it is solving a simple problem. The investigator recorded the electrical activity in both the hippocampus and the nearby entorhinal cortex from electrodes that were permanently implanted there. While the animals were learning in which arm of a Y-maze to obtain food, electrical waves developed that started in the hippocampus and spread to the adjacent entorhinal cortex. After the cats had solved this simple problem, their performance in the maze was now associated with a rhythmic electrical activity that arose instead in the entorhinal cortex and spread into the hippocampus. While this finding does not tell us how the hippocampus functions in the storage of memories, it does provide a starting point for studying the change in electrical relations between the hippocampus and connected structures during learning.

When investigators realized that the hippocampus was important for human memory, they started to study memory and learning ability in hippocampally damaged animals. They hoped that the greater variety of surgical lesions possible in experimental animals would help explain how the hippocampus performs its job. Surprisingly, however, hippocampal damage in animals has not consistently led to any obvious loss of recent memory. For example, we have already seen that rats learn an active avoidance response perfectly well after bilateral hippocampal damage. These animals clearly remember what they have learned from one training trial to the next (typically one minute intervenes), or they would not be able to master the problem. On the other hand, rats with hippocampal damage do indeed seem to be deficient at learning and remembering complex maze problems. Even these deficits in maze performance are only partial, since the rats eventually are able to learn the complex maze. Similarly, when experimenters damage the hippocampus after rats already have learned a maze problem, only a partial retrograde amnesia develops and the animals relearn the task normally with additional practice. The memory loss may be partial because the hippocampus, difficult to approach surgically, may not have the right kind or amount of experimental damage or, alternatively, other brain centers may partly substitute for the hippocampus in such lower animals as the rat.

Even in the monkey, with a brain quite similar to man's, experiments have so far not shown that the hippocampus is crucially necessary for normal learning and memory. Monkeys with bilateral hippocampal damage are not at all retarded in learning to solve a simple visual problem, even when the individual training trials are separated by long periods of time. Some experimenters have found, however, that monkeys with hippocampal damage are specifically deficient at learning tasks that require them to perform responses in a certain sequence. For instance, monkeys with hippocampal lesions have particular difficulty in solving a problem that requires them to alternate two different responses in a regular sequence. As we have already seen, studies of cats with hippocampal damage also are ambiguous in respect to the importance of the hippocampus for memory. These operated cats do not retain the ability to perform an active avoidance response that was learned before their brain operation, but nevertheless they usually can relearn the response after surgery if they are given enough practice.

There are at least two possible explanations for the differences between the reported effects of hippocampal damage in man and in infrahuman animals. For one thing, even in people the memory loss following hippocampal damage is not absolute. It can be partly overcome by the repetitious study of material that is to be memorized. The training procedures commonly used to test learning ability and memory in animals are precisely of this repetitious sort. The behavioral tests commonly used with animals thus may not be sufficiently sensitive to detect the loss in recent memory that so clearly follows hippocampal damage in man. This possibility receives strong support from a recent study of mice that were taught an extremely simple position-habit which they could learn in *one* trial. No repetitious practice was needed. Prompt damage to both hippocampus and entorhinal cortex resulted in the eradication of the recently learned habit; the mice automatically switched back to an older position-habit, previously learned in the same apparatus.

It is also possible that the crucial role of the hippocampus in the memory processes of man represents an evolutionary shift in the functioning of this limbic structure. Compared to infrahuman animals, there are some anatomical changes that are seen in the human hippocampus and its connections. The relative number and complexity of its cells are increased in the human brain and the nerve fibers in the human fornix bundle (one of the primary connections between the hippocampus and the rest of the brain) are notably increased in number, even as compared to the general increase in the number of fibers seen in other major tracts in the brain of man.

The mammillary bodies (see Figure 2–8), small limbic structures in the hypothalamus, are directly connected with the hippocampus; they also may be important for memory processes in man. Chronic alcoholics, suffering from longterm nutritional deficiency, frequently develop severe losses of recent memory and, in such cases, pathologists typically find damage in and around the mammillary bodies. As in the case of the hippocampus itself, however, a memory function for these small hypothalamic structures has not yet been demonstrated convincingly in experimental studies of animals.

REFERENCES

Anand, B. K., G. S. Chhina, and Baldev Singh (1962). Effect of glucose on the activity of hypothalamic "feeding centers." *Science*, **138**, 597f.

Bard, Philip (1929). A diencephalic mechanism for the expression of rage with special reference to the sympathetic nervous system. *American Journal of Physiology*, **84**, 490–515.

Beach, F. A. (1947). Evolutionary changes in the physiological control of mating behavior in mammals. *Psychological Review*, **54**, 297–315.

Brady, J. V. (1961). Motivational-emotional factors and intracranial electrical self-stimulation. In D. E. Sheer, ed., *Electrical Stimulation of the Brain*. Austin: University of Texas Press. Pp. 413–430.

Cannon, W. B. (1934). Hunger and thirst. In Carl Murchison, ed., *A Handbook of General Experimental Psychology*. Worcester, Mass.: Clark University Press. Pp. 247–263.

Delgado, J. M. R., W. W. Roberts, and N. E. Miller (1954). Learning motivated by electrical stimulation of the brain. *American Journal of Physiology*, **179**, 587.

Doty, R. W. (1961). Conditioned reflexes formed and evoked by brain stimulation. In D. E. Sheer, ed., *Electrical Stimulation of the Brain*. Austin: University of Texas Press. Pp. 397–412.

Fuster, J. M. (1958). Effects of stimulation of brainstem on tachistoscopic perception. *Science*, **127**, 150.

Gloor, Pierre (1960). Amygdala. In John Field, H. W. Magoun, and V. E. Hall, eds., *Handbook of Physiology, Section I: Neurophysiology*, Vol. II. Washington, D.C.: American Physiological Society. Pp. 1395–1420.

Grossman, S. P. (1960). Eating or drinking elicited by direct adrenergic or cholinergic stimulation of hypothalamus. *Science*, **132**, 301f.

Herrick, C. J. (1933). The functions of the olfactory parts of the cerebral cortex. *Proceedings of the National Academy of Sciences*, **19**, 7–14.

Hess, W. R. (1954). *Diencephalon: autonomic and extrapyramidal* functions. (*Monographs in Biology and Medicine*, Vol. III.) New York: Grune & Stratton.

Jasper, H. H. (1960). Unspecific thalamocortical relations. In John Field, H. W. Magoun, and V. E. Hall, eds., *Handbook of Physiology, Section I: Neurophysiology*, Vol. II. Washington, D.C.: American Physiological Society. Pp. 1307–1321.

Kaada, B. R. (1960). Cingulate, posterior orbital, anterior insular and temporal pole cortex. In John Field, H. W. Magoun, and V. E. Hall, eds., *Handbook of Physiology, Section I: Neurophysiology*, Vol. II. Washington, D.C.: American Physiological Society. Pp. 1345–1372.

Kleitman, N. S. (1963). *Sleep and Wakefulness* (rev. ed.). Chicago: University of Chicago Press.

Klüver, Heinrich, and P. C. Bucy (1939). Preliminary analysis of functions of the temporal lobes in monkeys. *Archives of Neurology and Psychiatry*, 42, 979–1000.

Lashley, K. S. (1929). *Brain Mechanisms and Intelligence*. Chicago: University of Chicago Press.

Lindsley, D. B. (1960). Attention, consciousness, sleep and wakefulness. In John Field, H. W. Magoun, and V. E. Hall, eds., *Handbook of Physiology, Section I: Neurophysiology*, Vol III. Washington, D.C.: American Physiological Society. Pp. 1553–1593.

MacLean, P. D. (1960). Psychosomatics. In John Field, H .W. Magoun, and V. E. Hall, eds., *Handbook of Physiology, Section I: Neurophysiology*, Vol. III. Washington, D.C.: American Physiological Society. Pp. 1723–1744.

Magoun, H. W. (1963). *The Waking Brain* (2nd ed.). Springfield, Ill.: Charles C Thomas.

Morgane, P. J. (1961). Distinct "feeding" and "hunger motivating" systems in the lateral hypothalamus of the rat. *Science,* 133, 887f.

Moruzzi, Giuseppe, and H. W. Magoun (1949). Brainstem reticular formation and activation of the EEG. *Electroencephalography and Clinical Neurophysiology,* 1, 455–473.

Olds, James (1962). Hypothalamic substrates of reward. *Physiological Reviews,* 42, 554–604.

Olds, James, and Peter Milner (1954). Positive reinforcement produced by electrical stimulation of septal area and other regions of rat brain. *Journal of Comparative and Physiological Psychology,* 47, 419–427.

Olds, M. E., and James Olds (1963). Approach–avoidance analysis of rat diencephalon. *Journal of Comparative Neurology,* 120, 259–315.

Papez, J. W. (1937). A proposed mechanism of emotion. *Archives of Neurology and Psychiatry,* 38, 725–743.

Richter, C. P. (1942–1943). Total self-regulatory functions in animals and human beings. *Harvey Lectures,* Series 38, 62–103.

Stellar, Eliot (1960). Drive and motivation. In John Field, H. W. Magoun, and V. E. Hall, eds., *Handbook of Physiology, Section I: Neurophysiology,* Vol. III. Washington, D.C.: American Physiological Society. Pp. 1501–1527.

Teitelbaum, Philip, and A. N. Epstein (1962). The lateral hypothalamic syndrome: recovery of feeding and drinking after lateral hypothalamic lesions. *Psychological Review, 69,* 74–90.

Thompson, Robert (1963). Thalamic structures critical for retention of an avoidance conditioned response in rats. *Journal of Comparative and Physiological Psychology, 56,* 261–267.

Young, W. C. (1961). The hormones and mating behavior. In W. C. Young, ed., *Sex and Internal Secretions* (3rd ed.). Baltimore: Williams & Wilkins. Pp. 1173–1239.

Young, W. C., R. W. Goy, and C. H. Phoenix (1964). Hormones and sexual behavior. *Science, 143,* 212–218.

INDEX

acquisition score, 124
active avoidance response, 124–130
adaptive behavior, cortex and, 2
ADH, *see* antidiuretic hormone
adipsia, 62
adrenergic compound, stimulation with, in hypothalamus, 63
afferent tract, 16
alcoholism, memory loss in, 135
amnesia, retrograde, 132
amphetamine, as appetite depressant, 60
amphibian, brain of, 20–23
amygdala, 68, 115, 121; complex behavior and, 130–135; damage to, 121, 130–135; flight and defense responses to stimulation of, 119; medial, 105
Anand, B. K., 60
animals, adipsic, 61–62; aphagic and hyperphagic, 58–59; brain-damaged, 4–5, 69; brain stimulation in, 9–12, 92–102, 115–120; cingulate gyrus damage in, 126–128; emotionality in, 121; fear-motivated behavior in, 123–130; fistulated, 65; flight behavior in, 119–120; frontal-lobe damage in, 7; intracranial self-stimulation in, 92–102, 107; lever-pressing response of, 92–102, 115–120; limbic stimulation in, 118–120; mating behavior of, 68–69; rage in,

121–122; selective attention in, 86; sleep–wakefulness cycles in, 75–86
antidiuretic hormone (ADH), 43, 65
aortic artery, 47
aortic receptors, 48–49
aortic sinus, 46
aphagic animals, 59
arousal, thalamic, 84; tonic versus phasic, 81
arousal system, forebrain, 72–89
ARS, *see* ascending reticular system
ascending reticular system (ARS), 25–30, 73–75, 80; afferent input of, 26–27; sensory systems and, 86–89; in sleep–wakefulness cycle, 80–82; thalamic level of, 83–86
association areas, of cortex, 6–8
"attention response," 118–119
auditory attention, 87
auditory cortex, 5
autonomic nervous system(s), 13; hypothalamus and, 39; sympathetic and parasympathetic, 40
avoidance response, *see* active avoidance response; conditioned avoidance response; passive avoidance response
awareness, behavior and, 74
axon, of nerve cell, 15, 17, 43